The Golden Spiral & Flower of Life Series

Volume One

Nature's Medicine Code

How Understanding The Simple Mathematics of the Universe Brings You Back To Health

"If you loved Ultra-Processed People, this is the book you need to read next"

Danica Apolline-Matić

"Danica seamlessly incorporates scientific data, age old principals, her personal journey of discovering these treasures and practical applications of creating health into her well researched and easy to read book that applies science and theory to the everyday. A valuable read for everyone!"

Micheline Edwards
Transformational Coach
Women's Health & Wellness Consultant, Advocate
Family Enrichment Specialist
Former Midwife, Doula & L.C

"I did not know what to expect when I picked up a copy of Nature's Medicine Code. I have read it in two sittings and I must say I was blown away! It is genius. The theory of the world being a perfect mathematical structure is not new (as mentioned by the author), but to connect it with the food we eat, chemicals we inhale and thoughts we think is simply brilliant. It is also eye opening. I enjoyed the section with practical advice on healthier life and I admit I have learnt new facts, such as banks being connected to war, teflon in kids uniforms and some leading 'eco' brands being actually toxic. I found Danica's arguments on meat and dairy industries, fossil fuels and mental health very interesting, and also very powerful.

The book is easy to read, well researched and comes with a pinch of humor. I must say it was refreshing to read on this subject without being showered with doom and gloom. It actually brings hope and provides a tool to change the world for better -the knowledge. Because when we 'know' we can take action. And when we are taking action, we become a change in the world. We are all individuals, but we are a part of the same orchestra."
                                                              - Gosia Charysz

"I really enjoyed this book. I found it useful, readable and well re-searched.
Before reading, I looked at the other reviews and noticed someone labelled it 'new age nonsense'. Please please please do not pay any attention to that review. Nothing could be further from the truth. The author presents a fascinating theory at the start of the book. I thought it was credible. However, even if you don't, it doesn't detract from the wealth of useful and well researched information crammed into the second half of the book.
After reading, I'm going to make some changes which, I know, will im-prove my life. Can you ask for anything more from a non fiction book? Highly recommended."
                                                        - Joe Barnes

"A fresh, informative, and inspiring read!
The way this book is written makes it a very easy and enjoyable read. With the author's experience interwoven within the principles it makes it much more than an informative and educational read it's an inspir-ing guide to health and wellness, showing the logical and magical pat-terns within nature and how we can utilise this to understand how best to nurture our health and take a new view on medicine.
I found it explained the principles in a very accessible way that I could understand and provided and very enjoyable read!"
                                                        - Sophie Joseph

"Fantastic book! Written in a totally accessible style and has such in-teresting insights into the relations between maths, health, music - a really fascinating read"   - Denis Fernando

First Published in Great Britain in 2018 by Danica Apolline
Second Edition 2024

978-0-9575721-4-0

www.danicaapollinematic.co.uk

The information given in this book should not be treated as a
substitute for professional medical advice; always consult a medical
practitioner. Any use of information in this book is at the reader's
discretion and risk. The author cannot be held responsible for any loss,
claim or damage arising out of the use, or misuse of any key of this
book or the suggestions made or the failure to take medical advice.

Dedicated to our remarkable solar system, our beautiful planet, our beautiful medicinal plants and trees and all of nature, our beautiful bodies, our remarkable DNA and my beautiful boy.

For being living proof to me of what I share here.

Contents

In these usual times......

When I first wrote this book, we lived in a different world; a world before COVID, a time when some things, at least, were simpler.

What I share here still holds true, and is probably even more important now than it was then.

Whilst I haven't done much to update the book, since COVID, the principles remain even with all that the world and humanity has lived through. It felt important to acknowledge it as we begin, for are embarking on a journey all about health, life, nature, disease......and ultimately, love.

April 2024

Prologue

I have to start this book with an apology. I have something to tell you about it, but I need you to promise me that you will carry on reading it, even after I have told you this one thing. I promise you it will be worth it.

But first you have to promise.

Promise you'll carry on reading even after I have told you that one thing.

Pinky promise.

Have you promised?

OK.......now you can turn the page.

I am really sorry to have to tell you this, but this book is about mathematics. AND a little bit of science.

There. I said it.

And you promised! So I invite you to keep reading........and I promise to make it fun and interesting and all the things you never thought mathematics and science could be – mathematics and science you probably weren't taught at school, which if you had, you may have felt very differently.

I think this is the best mathematics and science – the *most awesome brilliant amazing* mathematics and science there is. It explains why you are the way you are, why the world is the way It is. And I have done everything I can to explain it simply and easily for you, and I hope I am introducing something that will make you say "wow".

So, I invite you to take my hand, and walk with me on a little journey of a number – just one number – which, when I explain what it is and how I think it works – might change how you think and feel about life, the world, your health (and maybe even, if I am lucky, about mathematics and science).

Here we go.......

"[The universe] cannot be read until we have learnt the language and become familiar with the characters in which it is written. It is written in mathematical language, and the letters are triangles, circles and other geometrical figures, without which means it is humanly impossible to comprehend a single word."

~ Galileo

Introduction

When I was 14 I was facing an important decision that would determine the course of my life. I had to choose which subjects I would study for my GCSEs, examinations taken in England by 16 year olds.

I had originally wanted to be a pilot. It was 1989, and we only had paper based snail mail, so I wrote a letter to British Airways, asking if they would consider applications from those of us who wore glasses, who had had corrective surgery to give us 20/20 vision. I had been wearing glasses since I was 8 years old, and laser surgery had only just started being trialled as a way of correcting vision. British Airways wrote back, and told me that, as there were no guarantees for the long term success of laser surgery, they were not accepting applications from anyone who had to wear glasses or had had corrective surgery – that 20/20 vision was a pre-requisite.

So that was that. That letter freed me to choose my other career option, and the subjects that would take me in that direction - Pharmacy.

I was fascinated by health, medicine and the body. I wanted to understand how substances in the body change the way it works – and to me medicine was the strongest example of how that happens.

I was randomly out shopping on our local High Street one Saturday afternoon with my Mum and siblings, and walked past a signed in Chemist shop window, looking for Saturday staff. I was 14 years old. My Mum gave a lovely smile, and a nudge, and 15 minutes later I had my first job.

I worked there Saturdays and holidays, and took every opportunity to sneak into the dispensary to help out, rather than to be filling shelves with shampoos and shower gels to be sold, which didn't interest me at all. But I *loved* the dispensary. I was fortunate to have my interest stoked by the wonderful pharmacist who managed the shop, and whenever I asked "what does this medicine do?", he directed me to the ABPI (Association of the British Pharmaceutical Industry) Datasheet Compendium or the BNF (British National Formulary), listing all of the pharmaceutical medicines in use in the UK at that time. I turned myself into a pharmacy assistant, and the pharmacist seeing my fascination, allowed me to do that always with a wise and kind and knowing smile. When he left, and another brilliant pharmacist joined, he continued the first pharmacist's good work, encouraging me to read and learn about the medicines I was learning to dispense. By the time I was 16 years old, I knew the brand names and generic names of almost every drug in the dispensary, their indications and contraindications. I knew what could be prescribed with what, and what would be dangerous to have prescribed together, and saw the importance of the role of pharmacists in checking the prescriptions issued by doctors. I remember the pride I felt on one occasion noticing on a prescription two drugs that had been prescribed together, that I knew shouldn't be and telling the pharmacist who beamed at me. School friends would bring me their prescriptions to talk about, and I had the nickname "Dr Dee".

At the age of 18 I went to University to pursue my love of medicine, studying my beloved subject of Pharmacy. My favourite moment in my first year was making aspirin tablets by hand. I had chosen to go to Manchester, a party city in the days of the famous Hacienda, and partied hard, so it was no surprise that I failed by first year exams, even though my love of my subject hadn't waned. A summer of intensive revision for my resits meant that I was well prepared, however my first ever panic attack happened in a resit and meant that I had to repeat my first year. For some reason that I have been unable to explain, I didn't pass that first year the second time either. I had settled down, worked hard, was bright enough, but for some reason just couldn't make it through the exams again. I have come to believe that had I completed my studies as a Pharmacist, and was a Pharmacist now, I wouldn't see and understand what I present in this book, so my feeling is that life was taking me in other directions to learn all I needed to learn that I share here.

I transferred to another subject of interest – Psychology, and completed my degree studies in that. After I finished University, I worked as a mental health keyworker with people with severe mental health problems such as schizophrenia and bipolar affective disorder, which I loved, but when my mother became terminally will with the cancer she'd had diagnosed while I was still at University, I realised I couldn't care for people in my work all day and care for my mother at home too. So I turned to another passion for me – training. I was a volunteer at University for an organisation that supported students using a listening telephone service, and ended up leading the training team that developed the volunteers. I loved running training courses, and seeing people have those "aha!" eureka moments when they realise what they are truly capable of – seeing people flourish in this way is something that still gives me goosebumps to this day.

My interest in health however remained. I was fascinated by the pictures of the map of the body depicted on the soles of the feet that led me to learn Reflexology, not long after I graduated. It was the time that I realised that there is much more to the understanding of health than we learn in the traditional western medical model of health and medicine. I was able to see, feel and treat physical conditions through giving these treatments, even though our current ways of looking at Anatomy and Physiology haven't yet enabled us to understand Eastern maps of the body and approaches to medicine.

When I began my Reflexology course, I had never even had a treatment or met anyone who had, I just wanted to understand what that map of the body on the feet was about. On the second week of the course, something happened that transformed by understanding of health, anatomy, physiology and science. We were taught about the spine. The spine, when you look at where it is represented in the feet, runs along the inside of each foot – along the length of each foot where your feet, when you put them together, meet. The amazing thing is that it *looks exactly like a miniature version of the spine in your back*. It is shaped, and curved in exactly the same proportions as the spine in your back. And, when you apply gentle pressure to it, as we were taught to do, you can count what feel like tiny little fish bones in the feet – these represent each of the individual vertebrae in the spine.

I thought this was *incredible*. I rushed home, and pinned down the first friend I saw into an armchair to give it another go on someone outside of my class. This person happens to have a scoliosis, an S-shaped curve in the back - which I had actually forgotten about until after I had applied the reflexology technique to their feet. Whilst gently "working on" the spine through this person's foot, I could map out and feel an S-shaped curve in the spine area of the foot – which was *precisely* in the same place, to the same curvature as the S shape in this person's spine in their back. My eyes nearly popped out of my head with amazement, excitement and wonder.

The map of the feet isn't the only place where the body as a whole, is represented in a smaller form, by the way. It is also represented in exactly the same way on the hands, and in the ears, and even in the eyes.

This, however, was a seminal moment for me when I realised that true models of health and medicine are more holistic, and that what I had been taught at school and in my Pharmacy degree was only part of the picture of what maintains health and treats disease.

This realisation has continued to be proven in my work using energy healing techniques such as Reiki, and personally witnessing instant healings of long-standing health conditions, including instant and visible changes to damaged bones. There is increasing evidence that proves that disease can be treated in many ways, including using energy, meditation, intention, and the mind.

My fascination with the influence of substances however, especially medicine, on the body however remained and it is this that I draw upon here.

I worked for a time with some of the most remarkable medical herbalists, naturopaths, homeopaths and nutritionists at a shop selling herbal remedies, homeopathy and food supplements, and came to understand more about medicine, and the use of medicine, food and nutrition. It was during this time that I had a realisation – a vision; an understanding of how mathematics and sound are important considerations in medicine – and it is this realisation that I share here. Less than a decade later, I became a homeopath. I used to be a sceptic - I thought it was a placebo, that people were just taking sugar pills because of my pharmacy background. My own health challenges and seeing what it could do for son, when he was a baby proved to me how powerful a medicine it truly is.

This is, ultimately, a Theory of the mathematics and music of medicine. It is the Theory of a Code that I think is the key to health, and to understanding whether the medicine we ingest will bring us health, or is a drug that will make us more sick.

What I share in this Theory doesn't just apply to medicine, it applies to food and toiletries we put on our skin and to all aspects of health.

It is a very simple Theory. There is some basic knowledge of the science and the mathematics of life that needs to be explained here in order for it to be understood. You made a promise to read it, and I have made a promise to make it as simple (and interesting) as I can, as it is my intention that everyone, from every background and level of education can understand it.

Before we go into the background to the Theory – and to the Theory itself – it feels important to address something really important about our relationship with science and scientists.

The role of scientists is crucial to the healthy future of us all. Scientists who are dedicated to researching possible advancements with rigour and dedication benefit all of us. As I write this, a week after the death of Stephen Hawking, one of the greatest scientists we have seen in the last hundred years, we are all remembering in awe what one person can accomplish – his achievements were truly remarkable.

Science and scientists are at the core of all progress, and there is wonderful work being done by many scientists to make the world of science accessible to everyone, opening the doors to how discoveries are made, as a way of helping us to build relationships with them and the vital work that they do.

However not all scientists – or science – is so open and transparent, and we have to both open our eyes to this, and to take action to preserve the integrity of science by supporting those scientists committed only to progress that benefits all of humanity – progress that does no harm.

More and more evidence is emerging of how research findings can be (and are) easily manipulated using statistics in ways that can hide or omit important findings, as we see unfortunately a lot particularly in drug research. Editor-in-Chief of *The Lancet,* the most well-respected medical journal in the world, Dr Richard Horton – who has been in his post for over 20 years - has publicly stated that "The case against science is straightforward: much of the scientific literature, perhaps half, may simply be untrue. Afflicted by studies with small sample sizes, tiny effects, invalid exploratory analyses, and flagrant conflicts of interest, together with an obsession for pursuing fashionable trends of dubious importance, science has taken a turn towards darkness."

This means that it is important that we learn to question everything we are told, to do the research for ourselves, to observe and notice what works for us and our families – and what doesn't - and to learn to listen to our feelings and our bodies as to what we sense is the best course of action for ourselves and our families, with the help of qualified professionals as needed.

Sometimes we can't prove – with the equipment and tools for measurement we currently have at our disposal in the modern scientific world – how what we see is good for our health works. Conventional medicine's inability to prove some aspects of what works in health doesn't mean it doesn't work, it just means that we haven't yet developed the technology we need to measure what our eyes and experience are showing us to be true, or the way in which the research is designed doesn't account for how differently some medicines and therapies work compared to conventional medicine, resulting in misleading and inaccurate data.

There are many large scale remarkable peer-reviewed, double-blind clinical studies proving the effectiveness and power of homeopathy and these are shared by the Homeopathic Research Institute (HRI). We are however told by the mainstream media, which is funded by vested interests including pharmaceutical companies that there is no evidence to support it.

People are increasingly turning to evidence that they see with their own eyes – evidence that might or might not be backed up by existing scientific data, at times that goes completely against what is the prevailing view of existing research as it is accurately - or falsely - presented. Our own eyes might see the opposite of what we are told by conventional science, and more and more of us are questioning what we are being told, and that can only ever be a wonderful thing.

Questioning minds and curiosity lead to advancements in science and medicine and in all of our lives.

So inherent in this Theory is an invitation to us all to reclaim science as something that is, and should be, accessible to us all. That curiosity that drives true scientists who recognise scientific research as a journey with many possibilities, open to exploring them all with an open mind is something we can all aspire to.

As in every time in history when new discoveries have been made, there are science fundamentalists who are no longer curious, or open to new ideas, who say that new discoveries and possibilities are "impossible" or the work of "pseudoscience". Anything that hasn't yet been proven or understood could be said to be "impossible" or "pseudoscience", Galileo and the other scientists proposing that the world is round would have had the same types of terms thrown at them too.

History is filled with examples of how progress has always been made with an open mind, curiosity and a willingness to consider new possibilities – to prove the seemingly "impossible". Those are the bedrock of true discovery, and true scientific thought.

And as I prepare to take you on a journey of wonder and discovery, I would like to offer one more suggestion – or observation. It is about *who* can be described as a scientist.

The Oxford Living Dictionary defines science as "the intellectual and practical activity encompassing the systematic study of the structure and behaviour of the physical and natural world through observation and experiment."

We are constant observers and experimenters – all of us. We observe the weather, and choose what clothes to wear that will keep us comfortable within it – we experiment with which of our clothes are the best to use. We observe what happens when we put different ingredients together to prepare our meals, and experiment until we are happy with what we have produced. We observe what happens to us and our loved ones when we and they are ill, and we experiment with different treatments until we (hopefully) find a treatment that works. As parents, we observe our children and experiment with (often many!) different approaches that might support the development of our children, until we find ones that we and they are happy with.

And so I believe that *all* of us are scientists. We are scientists every day, observing situations, asking questions about what might work, when and how, and experimenting to put those suggestions to the test.

True health can only be attained when we all understand what makes us healthy, and all understand how medicine truly works, and that means being more aware when observing what works and what doesn't, when trying different approaches to the problems and challenges that we face.

True health will be embraced in society when we walk alongside those curious open-minded professionals who are paid to practice science every day, and they alongside us, and that we share only one goal in mind together: health free of consequence, side effect or harm to people, the planet, and all of life on Earth.

So I have written this book – this Theory - with everyone in mind. It isn't written in an academic style, or using academic language, as it is my intention that everyone who would like to read it and have access to it does so.

My wish is that you enjoy it, and that at some point you have – as I did and do every day - a wow.

Part 1: Physical Medicines

A Journey into Mathematics

When I was a teenager, I used to love to listen to a song by De La Soul. *3 is the Magic Number* was one of those tunes I used to bop around to on my Walkman as I walked through my school corridors, going from lesson to lesson.

3 may well be a magic number, but there is a *much* more magic number than 3. It is the number Phi, symbolised by the Greek letter φ. It has a value of 1.61803399 (or 1.618 for short). It is known as the Golden Number, Golden Ratio or Golden Mean.

Pythgoras (570-495 BC) was an Ancient Greek teacher who invented mathematics and arithmetic – the basics of mathematics that we still learn today. He practised in the days where there was no separation between mathematics, science, music, philosophy and astronomy, and he studied and taught all of these. These subjects were understood to be linked to each other during his life 2,500 years ago, and a greater understanding is emerging that he and others who taught in this way were onto something.

Pythagoras studied the vibration of strings as he plucked them on a musical instrument called a lyre.

In those days, 7 was considered to be the "magic number" for everything. Music was played using only a 7 tone scale. It was a mark of how respected Pythagoras as a teacher was, that he was successfully able to introduce another number of significance that altered the cultural perceptions of his time.

He identified that, when playing a 7 tone scale, it is possible to create a perfect harmony by adding an extra tone - a small half-step after the 4th tone. Even though he was going against the accepted wisdom of the ancient Greeks – that the number 7 is sacred – adding this extra tone makes an octave. The perfect octave creates what Pythagoras defined as *harmonia*.

The addition of this "fifth", as this special note is called leads not only to harmony, but also brings with it a mathematical ratio. Octaves and harmonies have embedded within them a remarkable number: the Golden Number Phi - 1.618.

There is more of an exploration about the mathematics of music and Phi in the Appendix, if you would like to read more, but for now, what we are talking about when we are exploring the mathematics of health is also the mathematics of harmonies as we hear them in music - Pythagoras' *harmonia*.

So what is this Golden Number and how is it relevant to us and to medicine, health & life?

In order to understand this, we need some help from another mathematician - a genius called Fibonacci who lived around 1000 years ago, during the "Middle Ages" in the Italian town of Pisa. Fibonacci discovered a mathematical sequence of numbers that when drawn into a pattern forms the Golden Spiral, or Fibonacci Spiral, which contains the number Phi.

The Fibonacci Sequence goes like this:

Start at 0 and count up, each new number is the sum of the previous 2 numbers. So the sequence goes like this:

0+1 = 1
1+1 = 2
1+2 = 3
2+3 = 5
3+5 = 8
8+5 = 13
8+13 = 21

and so on so the sequence looks like this:

0,1,1,2,3,5,8,13,21,34,55,89,144, 233......

If you divide one number in the Fibonacci sequence by the number before it, then you get Phi at any point from 89 onwards– or at the smaller numbers, a number very very very close to Phi. The further along the sequence you go, the closer and closer to the exact number of Phi you come.

When these numbers are drawn onto graph paper, with each number representing the size of the square a line is drawn in – so drawing across 1 square, then 1 square, then 2 squares, then 3, then 5, then 8 and so on carrying on using the Fibonacci sequence numbers, they form a pattern – it is a perfect ever growing spiral.

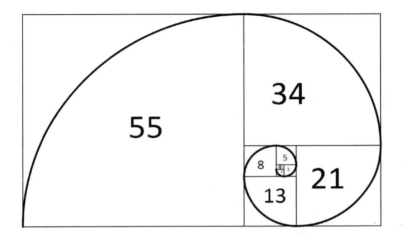

This spiral is called the Golden Spiral. It is a truly remarkable spiral, with the perfect geometric (mathematical) properties of Phi. This perfect mathematical spiral can be seen throughout nature, for example:

- In the famous nautilus
- In the proportions of our ears, how they grow and unfold
- The arrangement of faces, in particular the positioning of our mouth and nose along with our eyes and chin
- The proportions of the uterus
- In the spirals of the DNA
- In the growth and unfolding of leaves
- The number of petals a flower has
- The arrangement of seed heads, for example clearly seen in the sunflower
- The way in which branches on trees grow or split
- Animal bodies, including starfish, ants, honeybees, and the fins on dolphins
- How blood flows through blood vessels

- How hurricanes and tornados travel
- How currents flow in seas and oceans
- In the formation of ice crystals and snowflakes
- The Aurora Borealis (Northern Lights)
- How planets in our solar system orbit each other as they travel through the galaxy
- In how electrons flow around the nucleus of an atom[1]
- How the energy of balanced, healthy chakras flow

In fact, it has been proposed that phyllotaxis – the arrangement of leaves on a plant stem that follow the golden spiral – allows maximum levels of light capture, which maximises photosynthesis and plant growth.

This was proposed by Strauss et al.[2]

In 2012, John J. Wille found that even single-celled prokaryotes, some of our smallest microorganisms contain Fibonacci patterns, as do motile (moving) single-celled bacteria that also organise themselves into "dynamic growth patterns resembling Fibonacci patterns".[3]

The Pyramids in Egypt also have this geometry built into them, which suggests that they were designed in a very advanced way, and this geometry is found in the artwork of Michelangelo and Leonardo da Vinci. Some modern day artists and architects apply the principles of

---

[1] Winter,D, Donavan, B., and Jones, M. (2012) Compressions, The Hydrogen Atom and Phase Conjugation

[2] Strauss, S et al., (2019) Phyllotaxis: is the golden angle optimal for light capture? New Phytologist (2020) 225: 499-510

[3] John J. Wille (2012) Occurrence of Fibonacci umbers in development and structure of animal forms: Phylogenetic observations and epigenetic significance Natural Science Vol 4, 216-232

the Golden Spiral and the mathematics of Phi in their artistry and architectural design.

Another way in which Phi is found in nature is through Phi circles. By drawing circles with diameters the same size that follow the Fibonacci sequence (so in a line next to each other, starting with 0,1,2,3,5,then 8 and so on), they form a triangle with very precise mathematical angles in them. The angles of this triangle are found in the "V" formation in which birds fly. The Phi double-spirals are found in the pattern left in the sand after a wave recedes on a shoreline. This is because the flow dynamics of water, which of course follow all fluid dynamics, are Phi double-spirals, drawn out upon the surface of the shore. And the Phi circles form the basis from which fractals, and the holographic nature of the Universe, unfold.

The Mandelbrot Set

Before we further explore how medicine, health, science, music and mathematics meet, I will introduce one last important mathematical component of life - the Mandelbrot Set.

The Mandelbrot Set comes not from a mathematical sequence, but from an equation in Chaos Theory that measures the point at which order and chaos meet. That mathematical equation has been typed into computers and a visual pattern created. The image that results from the Mandelbrot set shows how, in everything, there is a repeating expression of the same pattern. In other words, you can see the code you have written, expressed as a beautiful picture, and then as you zoom in to one part of the picture, you find the whole pattern is repeated again within it. No matter how much you zoom in, you see the same pattern. It is very difficult to explain in words how awesome it actually looks.

At this point I would recommend that you watch a short 6 minute video on YouTube showing an amazing visual of what the Mandelbrot set looks like, and what happens when you zoom into the image that is shown. It is presented by Gregg Braden, a former NASA Astrophysicist who has been studying the DNA and the electromagnetic field alongside the HeartMath Institute in the U.S.

Type the following into the YouTube search function and the video will come up:

"Gregg Braden showing how the world functions as a hologram"

Once you have finished, carry on reading this, as it will make more sense.

Your body is the expression of a repeating pattern, just like the Mandelbrot set. This is what learning Reflexology demonstrated to me – that the repeating pattern of the body is found in smaller and smaller ways such as the feet, hands, ears and even eyes, as Iridologists and Acupuncturists learn.

It isn't just in the body that this fractal approach to the expression of life can be seen. Trees, which are crucial for the gaseous exchange of carbon dioxide for oxygen, are a much larger version of our own human lungs. The tree trunk looks like the trachea, with the larger branches like bronchi, smaller branches like bronchioles and leaves where gaseous exchange occurs like our alveoli, where gaseous exchange happens within our bodies.

As well as helping to prevent cancer, The New Scientist reported has reported how broccoli may also help the immune system to clean harmful bacteria from the lungs. A compound found in the vegetable is now being trialled as a treatment for people with lung disease. Broccoli also looks like a mini tree, and is an example of how this repeating pattern is expressed in food we put into our bodies.

Walnuts look like the brains they nourish, kidney beans look like the kidneys they nourish too.

When we see something that looks like the part of the body it is meant to heal, it is called *the doctrine of signatures.* To me, it is evidence that we are all connected to everything.

All of these examples contain with them the mathematical code found in all of life – Phi.

This is a helpful place to continue our connection to looking at the link between mathematics and music.

The Importance of Sound Vibrations

Every sound is an expression of a *frequency* of energy. Frequency is a measure of how many waves of light energy occur in a given moment of time – known as wavelengths. Colour is a narrow band of many frequencies, or wavelengths. Every frequency emits a sound even if we can't hear it with our human ears. We know this because dogs and other animals can hear sounds that we can't hear, like the dog whistle. So every frequency of energy has a sound, and a colour.

Manfred Clynes was a concert pianist who embraced a scientific career so that he could find out about the connection between music and emotion.

Manfred found that, irrespective of cultural, religious or racial differences, we all create emotions in the same ways. Emotions, it turns out, are emitted in waves. It turns out that the wave patterns of love are related to Phi – to 1.618. Anger and hate send out different wave patterns that do not contain Phi. Waves of love encourage life to grow and unfold, like the unfurling petals of a flower or the unfurling of our limbs in the womb. Waves of hate, on the other hand, do not contain the magic number of 1.618 and destroy.

The link between sound frequencies and Phi is evidenced by the science of cymatics, which generates visual images of sounds. "Kyma" in Greek means wave. Cymatics was first defined by a student of anthroposophy named Hans Jenny in the 1960s, although the principles are documented to have been studied as far back as the early 1600s by Galileo.

A membrane or metal plate that has sand, flour, powder, liquid or other visible small particles sprinkled on its surface, has sound vibrations played to it, and the sand, flour, powder or liquid will move to in respond to the sound vibrations, and where there is a harmonious sound, form patterns that are geometrically (mathematically) perfect, containing the 1.618 ratio.

Cymascope has produced these wonderful images of 12 piano notes, as commissioned by Shannon Novak, a New Zealand-born fine artist.

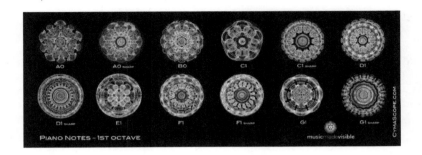

Harmonies reflect the 1.618 ratio of the Golden Spiral - and so are an expression of the Golden Spiral. So all that is harmonious - that the body understands and knows how to use and integrate - follows the perfect mathematical and musical expression of the Fibonacci sequence, the Golden Spiral and Phi. Any orchestra playing a perfect harmony can grow and welcome and integrate more instruments playing a harmonious sound. Welcoming a player playing a disharmonious note can throw the whole orchestra out of sync, if the player is playing a significant enough sound that is out of harmony, and out of alignment with these principles.

Further evidence of Phi mathematics & sound using water

Dr Masuro Emoto was a Japanese scientist who devoted the later years of his life to taking microscopic photos of ice crystals that form when water from different sources is frozen. Pure unpolluted water, when frozen, produces the most perfect stunningly beautiful water crystals – snowflakes – with perfect geometric patterns. Polluted water, when frozen, produces completely malformed crystals, with no geometry, no clear patterns, and have no clear form or shape to them.

Where his research gets really interesting is where he has taken photographs of ice crystals formed from ordinary water that has been sat in a glass jug over a piece of paper with the word "love" on it. And then water that has been sat on the word "hate". Water that just sits on the word "love" produces perfect and stunningly beautiful ice crystals, and yes, you guessed it, water sitting on the word hate freezes in the same malformed way as polluted water.

The ice crystals – snowflakes – of pure water, or water that is connected with love in some way have a perfect hexagonal geometry that contains within it. Phi. (1.618) is missing from the crystals formed from polluted or hate-filled water.

He also took photos and made videos of what happened when music was played to those ice crystals. Harmonious music (such as classical music) would cause the perfectly geometrical ice crystals to unfold like petals of a flower opening. Disharmonious music (such a rock music) would cause the ice crystals to lose their geometric properties. These videos can be easily found on YouTube for those who are interested in seeing these evidenced.

Dr Masuro Emoto inspired a new generation of experiments with water. Veda Austin, who lives in New Zealand, has taken up the mantle since, and teaches people how to very simply freeze water in a petri dish at home, and demonstrates through photographing the ice crystals that form, the remarkable messages in the water.

There is a version of Dr Masuro Emoto's work that you can try at home using rice. It's called the Love-Hate Rice experiment. It's great fun to do with kids. The instructions for how to do it are in the Appendix.

The Mathematics & Sound of Medicine, Food & Water

Imagine your body being like a large orchestra with all of the organs and structures representing the individual musicians in the orchestra, each producing their own sound, but together with the other musicians producing a beautiful piece of music – a symphony - when working harmoniously. The sound produced by the orchestra of our bodies may not be something we can easily hear using our human ears, but because everything is energy, and energy frequencies emit a sound, then everything emits a sound, including our body and the organs and structures within it. As I have already discussed, we know other sound frequencies exist simply through the example that dogs and other animals can hear frequencies we cannot hear.

When each organ and structure is healthy, together the sound that they make is like a harmonious symphony played by an orchestra.

We can welcome in new musicians to come and join in and contribute to the overall sound produced by the orchestra. Imagine, if you will, that we do that in terms of what we put into our bodies – in the food, medicines, water, products we put on our skin (that are absorbed into the body). If those substances carry a harmonious sound containing the geometry of life – the Golden Spiral – and the mathematics of Phi, then we will generate more of the harmonious orchestral sound. If however we ingest substances that are not harmonious, we will throw the orchestra (our body) out of sync. A disharmony will be generated that puts pressure on the other players (organs and structures) to bring the body back to harmony.

If any musician is negatively affected by what is taken into the body, it causes the sound they make to be off key - either sharp or flat, and so now the orchestra plays a disharmonious tune. The nearby organs and instruments hear the out-of-tune sound of their neighboring instrument, and either shudder and so themselves accidentally also play an out-of-tune note, or they try to work really hard to counter the effect by slightly altering their sound. This latter action puts pressure on the other instruments to do the same, and thus pressure is placed on the whole orchestra to try to get back to playing a harmonious tune, and sometimes they aren't able to do so, so the disharmony remains.

This is where the immune system comes in.

There is a really important aspect of our immunity that we have to mention here. It's the healthy bacteria that is found in the gut. 80% of the immune system is linked to the gut, so having a healthy gut is crucial to having a healthy immune system.

Imagine that, in the orchestra analogy, the bacteria represent the large string instrument section – all the violins, violas, cellos and double bases. There may even be a guitar or two.

And now imagine that the immune system is like the conductor of the orchestra. It knows when a sound is out of tune, and then makes decisions about how to overcome the disharmony. It may change the way the disharmonious musician is playing so that it no longer has an effect on the rest of the orchestra. It may invite the surrounding musicians to slightly alter how they are playing to adjust and neutralize the disharmonious sound. It may kick the disharmonious musician out even, if it is impacting on the rest of orchestra too negatively.

The immune system is designed to seek out anything that prevents the body from operating healthily, and remaining harmonious (in balance). It will either remove the problem or render it unable to have an effect. The immune system is designed to detect anything that is disharmonious to the body. If the body grows, exists and maintains itself using the mathematical and sound properties of harmony (Phi: 1.618), then the immune system is designed to nullify or remove anything that disrupts that harmony.

But in the same way that the immune system can't easily combat challenges without a healthy gut, the conductor can't fix the problems caused when a beautiful symphony is out of tune if the whole string section of the orchestra has gone and left the orchestra.

The conductor can't play a symphony without his string section – and cannot tell if the symphony being played by the remaining musicians is harmonious because he can't hear the whole symphony, one whole section of the orchestra, and sound of the symphony is missing. There is a hole in the orchestra, in the ability to play harmonious music, and this affects every other part of the orchestra which can't do it's job properly as hard as it tries.

What impacts the immune system? Let's take the example of cancer. Every cell in the body has a time to live and time to die, and new healthy cells come along and continue the process of keeping the body alive. Cancerous cells are those that haven't died when they are supposed to, for whatever reason, and continue to grow. We have cancerous cells popping in and out of existence all the time in our bodies, and a healthy immune system will easily detect those cells, and then go and destroy them. When the immune system is compromised or overloaded, it doesn't have the strength to also seek and destroy the cells that have become cancerous.

The theory that follows explains what can impact the healthy functioning of the immune system.

So having a healthy immune system – a healthy conductor who can detect all the disharmonious notes – becomes crucial.

What makes an immune system healthy?

1) Giving it only medicines, foods, and using toiletries and cleaning products that support and encourage health. We will come to explore these these steps.

2) A healthy gut. As we have said, 80% of the immune system is linked to a healthy gut. A healthy gut, with a healthy population of a range of strains of gut bacteria could be said to be like the conductor's manuscript. When the immune system has a healthy gut, it can function well. A conductor of an orchestra needs his or her manuscript from which he or she can successfully conduct the orchestra to play harmonious music.

3) Regular exercise.

4) Time spent outdoors in nature.

5) Reducing stress as much as possible,

Before we come to the role of medicine, and how it impacts the body, there are two more final pieces of knowledge about music to consider.

The Solfeggio Frequencies

The Solfeggio Frequencies are each part of an ancient 6-tone scale that have used in sacred music, such as Gregorian chanting. Originally developed by a Benedictine Monk, Guido D'Arezzo (991-1050 AD), each frequency can be used for healing, and each tone represents a particular aspect of health that can experience healing. They are as follows:

396 Hz – Liberating Guilt and Fear

417 Hz – Undoing Situations and Facilitating Change

528 Hz – Transformation and Miracles (DNA Repair)

639 Hz – Connecting / Relationships

741 Hz – Expression / Solutions

852 Hz – Returning to Spiritual Order

The tones were hidden until they were rediscovered by Dr Joseph Puleo in 1974. He applied a Pythagorean method to calculating the frequencies, and in the process discovered a further 3 tones:

174 Hz – Alleviating Stresses

285 Hz – Rejuvenation

963 Hz – Pineal Gland and Connection to Source

The Solfeggio Frequencies contain the principles of Phi and the Golden Spiral. The Theory explains the relevance of the Solfeggio frequencies in medicine and food.

The Schumann Resonance

Jan Wicherink, in his book *Souls of Distortion Awakening* describes the work of Daniel Winter. Daniel is a researcher who has studied the Schumann Resonance, and the Schumann waves that make up the Schumann Resonance, and has identified that the trees act as antennae for these frequency waves to connect with the Earth. This is an electromagnetic resonance that exists in the ionosphere around the Earth – between 30 miles above the surface of the Earth to the edge of space, about 600 miles up. In 1954 Schumann and H.L. König detected that the Schumann Resonance of the Earth is 7.83Hz, or as ancient Indian gurus said, is the frequency of Ohm. Our heart and brain patterns – again linked to Phi – are also linked to the Schumann Resonance of the Earth. Jan gives the remarkable description of how NASA spacecraft are all fitted with equipment that mimics these Resonances. Without a connection to these resonances – known as the "Heart Beat of the Earth", astronauts because distressed and confused, something that William Shatner, the actor who played James T. Kirk in the original Star Trek, experienced on his trip to space as a 90 year old in 2021, and shared in his book *Boldly Go: Reflections on a Life of Awe and Wonder.*

Life is expressed through waves of Light. These waves, including the Schumann Waves have a sound and a colour, as do all frequencies as we have discussed. The perfect alignment – a *harmony* – occurs when all of them work in alignment with Phi, the Golden Number.

Now that we have explored all of these areas, it is time to get to medicine.

How medicines work at a basic level

What I have come to understand about medicine and their impact on the body will be easier to explain once I have described how both herbal medicines and pharmaceutical drugs work using the examples of the herb Meadowsweet and the drug aspirin.

Each plant medicine, including commonly used herbs like chamomile, or peppermint, has a large number of different plant chemicals ("phytochemicals") working together synergistically to support health and wellbeing. In some cases, the number can be over 100 different plant chemicals working together.

Meadowsweet is a plant medicine that contains salicylic acid – a precursor to acetylsalicylic acid (aspirin). Both aspirin and meadowsweet can be used for pain relief, reducing fevers and inflammation. Whereas a side effect of the prolonged use of aspirin can be the development of a stomach ulcer, one of the main reasons meadowsweet is used is *for treating stomach ulcers.* It, like all herbal medicines, contains natural plant chemicals that treat and support many aspects of health at the same time.

Most pharmaceutical drugs are developed using research into plant medicines. The different chemicals in a plant are identified, and then one of the many, many plant chemicals is isolated based on which one scientists identify as the single plant chemical that most successfully treats a condition or disease in the body. That one plant chemical is then replicated again and again and then made into a pill. So instead of getting a combination of many, many different chemicals working together synergistically in a plant medicine, generating a harmony, you get just one chemical by itself, that has been synthetically replicated, in most cases in a pharmaceutical drug.

This knowledge forms the basis of this Theory on Mathematics, Music, Medicine & Health, which can now be shared. But before we do, it is important to mention the impact that all substances we use in our lives have on our body and health too.

Foods, toiletries, food supplements & Phi

If we understand that nature, in its purest form, contains the perfect mathematical and geometric properties of Phi, the Golden Spiral and the musical harmonies that are reflected by them, then this can be applied to our food also. Unadulterated food will grow and contain the properties of Phi and the Golden Spiral, and harmonious sound frequencies.

The same is true of natural plant oils that can be used for cleansing, and of vitamins and minerals that are extracted from a natural food source.

Food supplements that are made by isolating one vitamin or mineral and reproducing the chemical follows the same principles of producing pharmaceutical drugs.

Pesticides involve the use of one or a small number of individual chemicals spread over the surface of food, or designed to be integrated into a food, that does not have the geometric and mathematical properties of Phi – or an associated sound of harmonia. And so eating foods grown using pesticides triggers an immune response as the body thinks a foreign object has been ingested.

The same is also true of artificially made chemicals, petrochemicals, agrochemicals, cleaning chemicals, chemically produced food supplements, and foods and food products that are genetically modified or artificially produced in a laboratory.

Before we come to the Theory, there is one more piece of knowledge to share with you. This is where we come to some simple principles from science.

A Sojourn into Science

You may think of yourself as solid, dense, physical matter, but actually all of us are mainly made up of space. This is how.

We are physically made up of atoms. They look like this.

The physical matter of an atom is its nucleus – that bit in the centre – the rest surrounding it is energy. That physical matter in an atom only accounts for 1% of the atom - the other 99% is space - or energy. So that means that you, as something made of atoms, is therefore 1% physical matter and 99% space.

Marcus Chown in his book *Quantum Theory Cannot Hurt You,* gives the amazing statistic that, if all of the space within atoms and between atoms was removed, 99.99% of the entire population of the world – 99.99% of over 7 billion of us – would fit into the size of a sugar cube. Amazing, isn't it?!

So what is that space filled with? It is filled with energy.

How do we know there is this pool of energy? Dogs can hear sounds that we can't hear. Infrared light is a light frequency that we can't see with our physical eyes, but science measures sound frequencies and light frequencies that we as humans can't experience with our physical bodies. These frequencies are an expression of energy. So there is so much energy – so many frequency vibrations – that we don't experience physically but that we can measure and so know exist. The world is made of more than we can physically sense. These frequencies that we can't see or hear don't just exist outside of ourselves, they exist within us too.

Your thoughts, your feelings and your beliefs live in the energy within and around you. When you feel a little bit sick about something you know you have to do, but don't want to, you might feel it in your body a bit, but there isn't an organ that we can measure that says "this is the bit where dread lives". But we feel dread within us, and just outside of our physical bodies – dread is a feeling that we often sense in the air directly in front of our stomach. The same is true of "butterflies in our stomach". We feel these not just within our stomachs, but we can feel it in the space and the air in front of our bodies. The same happens with joy. We can't *measure* it in our bodies, but we might feel light as a feather, a lightness *within and around* us. Our feelings – and our thoughts - exist but are not contained within any one body system. That is because they don't live there. They live in the vast amounts of *space* that I have described, the 99% that isn't physical matter. In other words, our thoughts, feelings and beliefs are part of the energy within and around us.

This space – this energy – is known as the electromagnetic field, as is being studied by the HeartMath Institute in the U.S. It has measured that the electromagnetic field extends to up to 20ft from the heart.

The space within us and the space around us is filled with the energy made by a vast number of tiny light particles – they are called photons. Photons are the smallest quantum particles we know (mega tiny compared to atoms). We all have the same energy within and around us – this is the energy that quantum physicists study.

We are all made of this same energy, and so are completely connected to each other because we simultaneously all come from it at the same time. This energy is something that we know as the Zero Point Field. This Field is filled with photons. They are all in a constant tiny state of motion, communicating with each other, popping in and out of existence, *fluctuating and changing.* This is known as *The Uncertainty Principle* by Heisenberg. This means that there is this huge soup of connected photons all generating, through their combined energies, a huge collective mass of energy. Science journalist Lynne McTaggart, in her book *The Field*, quotes physicist Richard Feynman's description of the power of this combined energy. He gave the comparison that the energy in a single cubic metre of space (which includes the air around us) is enough to boil all the oceans of the world.

This is how, to quote Albert Einstein "everything is energy". Einstein, Nikola Tesla and Isaac Newton (after his work on gravity), three of the greatest scientists who ever lived were fascinated by energy, by quantum physics, by an understanding that we are more – much more – than physical matter.

Can Phi and the Golden Spiral be found in atoms?

Dan Winter in his paper *Compressions, The Hydrogen Atom and Phase Conjugation* has identified an equation proving that Phi, the Golden Number is found in the ratio of protons (positively charged particles in the nucleus of an atom) to electrons (negatively charged particles that flow around the nucleus) in an atom, and that the flow of electrons follows the Golden Spiral.

Now that we have all of the background knowledge of mathematics and science we need to understand this Theory of Medicine, it is time to present it to you.

The Theory on Mathematics, Music, Medicine & Health

Everything that I have described so far can now be summarized in this Theory.

Nature's Medicine Code is Phi (1.618) and is expressed in the geometry of the Golden Spiral and in the sound vibrations of harmonious sounds (a harmonia), including the Solfeggio frequencies and Schumann Resonance.

The healthy human body is itself an expression of Nature's Medicine Code and:

1) Substances we ingest, absorb or inhale either contain Nature's Medicine Code or they do not in either how the particles are arranged, or in the flow of electrons and energy of that substance.

2) Any substance whether it is in the form of medicine, food, or a substance applied to the skin, is "read' by the immune system in terms of its mathematics and musical sounds. If the substance contains Nature's Medicine Code, the properties of Phi, the Golden Spiral and a harmonious sound, the immune system recognises it as healthy to the body.

    This applies to food, drink, medicine, supplements, airbourne particles, or substances absorbed through the skin into the bloodstream (for example toiletries, cleaning products and cosmetics).

3) Any substance that doesn't contain Nature's Medicine Code, that is lacking the properties of Phi, the Golden Spiral and a harmonious sound, will be seen as a "foreign body" and potentially disease-causing by the immune system, which then will attempt to remove the substance.

This also applies to food, drink, medicine, supplements, airbourne particles, or substances absorbed through the skin into the bloodstream (for example toiletries, cleaning products and cosmetics).

4) The plant chemicals found in whole plants that support health contain Nature's Medicine Code. These are recognised by the body and used to promote health and wellbeing.

The plant chemicals work synergistically, and together create a larger Golden Spiral. The sound frequencies of the plant chemicals working together form a harmony. This is *harmonious medicine* and seen and felt by the body to promote life.

5) Pharmaceutical medicines, and synthetic chemicals made using the replication of one chemical, do not contain Nature's Medicine Code; the properties of Phi, the Golden Spiral or emit harmonious sounds.

The production of food using agrochemicals, pesticides, herbicides, GMOs or any other means that alters its genetic leads to "foods" that also do not contain Nature's Medicine Code. They are isolated chemicals, that emit a sound frequency that is not harmonious – indeed sound like a "dud note" to the body. These are *disharmonious substances.* The immune response, and the attempt to remove the perceived "foreign object" from the body causes pressure on individual organs, homeostasis and the body as a whole. This pressure results in side effects in the patient, some of which can be disabling or life-threatening in the short or long term.

The same is also true of artificially made chemicals, petrochemicals, agrochemicals, pesticides, cleaning chemicals, chemically produced food supplements, and foods and food products that are genetically modified or artificially produced in a laboratory.

As many as 100 plant chemicals (sometimes more) are, according to this Theory, arranged physically and/or in how the energy and electrons flow to form a perfect Golden Spiral. Within it will be found the mathematics of Phi = 1.618, and it will emit a perfectly harmonious sound. To the body, all medicines, foods & toiletries with this Nature's Medicine Code are a source of health.

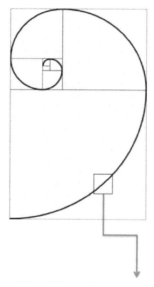

A pharmaceutical drug will be made based on taking one isolated plant chemical out of the 100 or so in the whole plant and then replicating it again and again. There is no Golden Spiral, no Phi mathematics, and no harmonious sound being emitted, in fact - to the body, it is like a "dud" note. The body therefore thinks it is a foreign object to be removed, and the immune system is activated.

6) Physical medicine can only successfully treat disease if it is harmonious.

7) Foods can only be nutritious and healthy to the body if they are harmonious.

8) In the case of foods and food products that are genetically modified and / or artificially produced in a laboratory, the DNA and / or structure of the food no longer contains Phi mathematics or the Golden Spiral and so the body cannot "read" what these are, and so treat these also as foreign objects that need to be removed using the immune system

9) Allergies to seemingly healthy foods can be caused by an overwhelmed immune system,; an immune system that has become confused by the excessive exposure to toxins and synthetic chemicals and so can no longer distinguish between harmonious medicine and food, and disharmonious substances. Babies and small children with allergies will have been exposed to those toxins and synthetic chemicals whilst in the womb, or will have inherited a sensitivity, intolerance or allergy (or both).

10) Cannabis (unadulterated pure organic cannabis), which is well documented as a treatment for serious conditions including cancers, autoimmune disorders, a range of neurological conditions including epilepsy, Alzheimer's and Parkinson's Disease, anxiety and depression, emits all of the Solfeggio frequencies.

11) When the immune system is working very hard to remove all of the many objects that the body sees as foreign from our food, toiletries and environment, it does not have the capacity to as easily also fight infections in the body, or to identify and remove cells that have become cancerous at an early stage. Cancers develop simply because the overworked immune system does not have the capacity to destroy cancerous cells at an early stage when it would otherwise be much easier for the immune system to do.

12) As it has been found that the mathematics of love is expressed as Phi (1.618), then the body is ultimately differentiating between all that is love, and all that is not love.

13) All that is grown, produced and made with love the body can use to support and maintain its health. Nature generally-speaking promotes the mathematical, geometric and sound frequencies of life and of love.

14) All that does not come from love will be rejected by the body if the body can, and if it can't will put pressure on the body causing side effects and cause illness. Synthetic pharmaceutical drugs, synthetic food supplements, pesticides, herbicides, GMOs, processed foods, synthetic chemicals, toiletries, and synthetic cosmetics are not an expression of love and so make the body sick.

Part 2: Energy Medicines

Nature's Medicine Code & Energy

In summary, this Theory suggests that the energy vibration and flow of every health-giving substance we ingest – medicine, food, toiletries, water – contains Nature's Medicine Code of Phi, the Golden Spiral and it's expression in the sound vibrations of a harmonia.

The energy flow of any substance we ingest that doesn't contain all of these aspects of Nature's Medicine Code will trigger an immune response as the body tries to get rid of it, and could lead to disease and ill health if the immune system is unable to do.

This is what I would suggest happens with physical medicines, but what about energy medicines?

Energy Medicines

So, as we have explored in the section on science, we are made of atoms. Atoms are only 1% physical matter, and 99% space (or energy – the electromagnetic field), therefore we are only 1% physical matter and 99% space (energy – electromagnetic field). That 99% space that we are made up of contains our feelings and emotions, which flow in and out of our experiences, in response to thoughts we have.

Energy medicines are medicines that are interested in working predominately with the 99% space, and through treating our energy or electromagnetic field, bring health to our emotions and feelings, and from there to our physical bodies.

Energy medicines bring about changes to our health emotionally, mentally and physically. These include homeopathy and Bach Flower Remedies. I will be explaining more about homeopathy in this Theory.

More "physical" medicines such as pharmaceutical drugs and herbal medicines also have an effect on our energy field; on our emotional and mental health too.

We can't always explain exactly how some energy medicines work, even though we see that they do. Our rational minds often need to understand something in order to accept its efficacy, but with some energy medicines, we haven't been able to fully explain how they work – yet. This is true of homeopathy. Yet there is a considerable amount of well-conducted, scientifically rigorous research that demonstrates – beyond any reasonable doubt – that homeopathy works, and the Homeopathy Research Institute is an international organisation specifically tasked with sharing the scientific developments and research of homeopathy around the world. Here however I will describe what I think is happening with homeopathic medicine. For anyone who thinks it is a placebo, I have addressed this in Part 4.

The Principles of Homeopathy

Homeopathy was discovered by a German medical doctor, Dr Samuel Hahnemann, I am always impressed by how its development has been helped by influential medical doctors and pharmacists who found that conventional medicine wasn't working well enough for their patients, or wanted to find a gentler, kinder, effective way of practising medicine.

My favourite is the story of Dr Hering who, whilst a medical student, was tasked with disproving homeopathy. He set about his task with zeal, but found he was unable to do so, instead becoming eventually completely convinced of its usefulness as a medicine and then practiced as a homeopathic doctor. He became hugely influential in the development of homeopathy. The Founder of Helios, one of the largest homeopathic pharmacies in the UK is a pharmaceutically trained pharmacist. Around 400 GPs in the UK practice homeopathy, and there is a professional body to represent the many doctors, pharmacists, midwives, vets and other conventionally trained medical professionals who are trained homeopaths. In the film *Magic Pills* by Ananda More, we see how in India more medical students choose to specialise in homeopathic medicine than in conventional or ayurvedic medicine, and it is the greatest form of medicine in both India and Cuba. *Inspiring Homeopathy* is a 2024 film that continues to share some of the amazing research into homeopathy.

It is part of the national health systems of not just India and Cuba, but Switzerland, Pakistan, Mexico, Brazil and Chile.

During the first COVID pandemic both the Indian and Cuban governments issued guidance for all of their citizens about which homeopathic remedies to take both for treating COVID, and prophylactically (as a preventative).

But what is it and what does it do?

A homeopathic medicine is a medicine that takes a substance and then dilutes it many many many times, so that there is no actual substance remaining in the medicine – just an energetic "hint", or imprint of it.

Homeopathy believes that the body knows how to heal itself, and that the remedies act as a catalyst to the body's "vital force" (life force) to then heal itself.

There are different ways in which homeopathy can be used, and some of these include:

- Constitutionally – giving remedies that match the personality profile of a patient. This reminds us of who we are, and brings us back to our core when we go out of balance, strengthening us
- Miasmatically – healing inherited traits be they physical or emotional. Epigenetics is a buzzword for what homeopaths have been working with for over two centuries!
- Therapeutically – using the "Law of Similars" – giving the body a remedy of a substance that would create the same symptoms that the sick person is experiencing.
- Life – clearing inherited trauma, and aligning more with living our path and purpose with greater ease
- Detoxification – to help the body clear toxins. It's a bit like the hair of the dog principle – giving a little energetic imprint of the toxin is like saying to the body "this is what is making you sick, now you know, you can clear it".

A substance that might be a medicine or a toxin when in full physical, "material" form is dissolved or diluted so that 1ml in 100ml is the substance, and the other 99ml is water. Then 1 ml of that diluted substance is added to another 99ml of water, making it another 1 part in 100. After 3 of these 1 in 100ml dilutions, there is no physical material left. A 6C dilution is 6 of these 1 in 100ml dilutions. 30C is 30 of these 1 in 100ml dilutions and 200C is 200 of these dilutions. It is possible to go up to 1000 dilutions, even 1 million!

If you imagine, the 6C dilutions (or potencies, as they are called in homeopathy), are those closer to the physical body. 30C has an effect further away from the body, going into the energy field. 200C has an effect further still, and the higher the potency, the further and further away from the physical and into the energy field we go.

We have already talked about how every energy frequency – vibration – has a corresponding sound (and colour). We have already begun using the orchestra analogy, but imagine again the whole body and all of the organs and structures, and all of the energy field around us (the 99% space in the atoms) operating as a big giant orchestra, thousands of individual musicians, when healthy, playing a beautiful symphony – a harmonia in Pythagoras' terminology. Of course there will be within that the prefect expression of Phi mathematics and Golden Spiral too.

When we give ourselves a physical medicine, it is like putting the biggest, loudest drum in the centre of the orchestra and going BOOM. Now, if the note of that drum, and the timing of that drumbeat fits with the other players of the orchestra, the sound will work synergistically – the orchestra will continue to play a harmonious tune. This is what medicine and food that contains the properties of Phi and the Golden Spiral does – even in a physical form, that medicine or food – or vibration - is recognised by the whole orchestra (body) which supports the continued playing of a harmonious piece of music by the whole orchestra. This is, I would suggest, what happens with the use of plant medicines.

Now imagine that that drum plays a BOOM that is totally out of harmony with the whole orchestra. The drum produces a note that doesn't fit with the music being played by the rest of the musicians and it doesn't contain the properties of Phi or the Golden Spiral. Because it has such a powerful effect on the workings of the whole orchestra, it throws the whole orchestra – the whole system – into disarray, with individual players trying to find where they were on their page to carry on playing, others feeling unable to withstand the power of the drum with their single small instrument. The individual musicians (individual organs and structures of our body) cease to function properly under the pressure of the big disharmonious BOOM. It throws the entire body – the physical and the energetic self – into disarray. Even the conductor (immune system) is shaken and needs help to recover. This is what is meant in the Theory above about disharmonious substances. This is, what I would suggest, happens with pharmaceutical drugs, synthetic chemicals in toiletries and cleaning products and food grown with the use of pesticides, herbicides or are GMOs.

Imagine now a different musician joining the orchestra. This musician plays a disharmonious tone, but this time this musician is playing a tiny little triangle, so no-one will really notice (apart from the surrounding players and the conductor). The conductor can quickly and easily take action to absorb and nullify the sound that the triangle player is playing so that the whole orchestra can easily continue playing a harmonia. The conductor might, for example, show the triangle player how to play the note correctly, and the conductor has been primed to listen out for the dud note from the triangle player so can quickly rectify any disharmony – any ill-effects.

Or, if the conductor is struggling to know how to get the orchestra back on track following the massive disharmonious, disruptive BOOM sound of the drum (caused by a disharmonious substance), a new musician, playing a tiny, gentle version of the BOOM gives the conductor the opportunity to say "Ah! I know what that is now! I know what to do!" and so can identify steps he can take to nullify the effects of the BOOM. The conductor gets back up on their feet and then either gets rid of the BOOM player or integrates it into the orchestra so that only a harmonious sound can be played by the whole orchestra together.

So homeopathy works in a similar way. It takes a substance, diluted many many many times so it is just an essence of that substance, and introduces it to the body. The body is designed to know how to make itself well (that is the purpose of the immune system), so it hears the vibration of that energy and the immune system (the conductor) says "Ah! Yes! I know what I need to do to bring the whole body (orchestra) into alignment so that the ill effects of that substance can be countered, the body return to health, and the orchestra continue playing its harmonia.

In conventional medicine, we *fight* diseases. We get into a battle, and do everything we can to squash any illness, with the might and power of pharmaceutical drugs if necessary. Diseases are definitely *bad* and to be defeated at all costs. In homeopathy and other natural medicines, diseases are an *invitation* to identify a weakness or imbalance in our health and/or lives and then to come to balance - and in the process this can strengthen the health of the whole person if they are ready to rebalance. In conventional medicine, the drugs are there to stop the disease, in plant medicine, the plants work together with the body to heal it, and in homeopathy, the medicines act as a catalyst to help the immune system know how to be strong again so it can heal the body and get rid of the disease itself.

Another way in which homeopathy can work can be summarised as follows.

Some substances that homeopathy uses would be toxic if ingested in full physical, material form. One homeopathic remedy for example, is belladonna, which is deadly nightshade. Deadly nightshade would make us very sick — very ill, even kill us, and usually there is a fever involved — but the homeopathic version can be used for teething babies and with fevers. The homeopathic version doesn't contain any of the substance that could make us sick, but putting in that teeny tiny energetic imprint of the substance — the energetic hint of the fever it generates — tells the immune system — the conductor — what to do to bring the body — the orchestra — back to a full harmonic sound and release any disease-causing effect of the illness or disharmony (in this case the fever). Deadly nightshade would be like the big booming disharmonious drum that would throw the orchestra into disarray by causing a big fever and possibly death. Homeopathic belladonna is like the little version of the drum that helps the conductor to identify how to respond to the effects of a disharmonious substance.

A similar approach is used in the thinking behind vaccination. However, many serious side-effects and illnesses are caused by bypassing the body's first line of defence (the skin), as well as introducing disharmonious substances in additives (adjuvants) like aluminium, formaldehyde and monosodium glutamate. There is more about this in the Steps to Healthier You.

Whereas pharmaceutical drugs are like the big disharmonious BOOM, often the conductor (the immune system), whilst a little wobbled will usually try to continue to function, even if with difficulty. In extreme cases, the conductor (immune system) has both arms and legs broken and has to try to continue to conduct with his limbs broken. He is so negatively affected that he no longer ceases to function properly at all.

So points to add to this Theory of medicine are that:

16) The sound vibration of any medicine has to be one that can be *absorbed and processed and integrated safely* by the body. If the disharmonious vibration is too great, disease will prevail as pressure is placed on the whole system.

17) The ability of a medicine to generate a harmonia (including the sound vibrations, mathematics and geometry of harmonia) is the key to successful safe effective health promoting medicine.

Part 3: Viruses & Bacteria

Our bodies take in not just foods, medicines and toiletries or chemicals, but disease-causing pathogens too – here I will be talking about viruses and bacteria.

What is interesting is that when you look at naturally occurring viruses, they are really very beautiful geometrically – in fact, they too have the perfect geometry of Phi and the Golden Spiral in them too.

Bacteria contain DNA and so also have the properties of Phi and the Golden Spiral within them too.

So if all things that bring us health contain Nature's Medicine Code, how do pathogens contain Nature's Medicine Code, yet still bring disease?

Let's explore this here.

Firstly, we need to address an assumption here. We assume that having an illness or a disease is *bad* and shouldn't happen, that we must bring to an end all pathogens.

Whilst of course none of us would want us or our loved ones to get sick, particularly not with anything *serious*, pathogens do exist in our ecosystem. We think we are at the top of the food chain, we have made it so – controlling the growth and variety of plants that we see, managing wildlife, growing animals purely for food in a way that is beyond the bounds of a balanced ecosystem. However it is a fact that we are *not* at the top of the food chain. Pathogens are.

From a purely evolutionary perspective, those of us with strong immune systems (and the support of useful medicines) will therefore use those experiences to strengthen us, while those in the species that are weaker will not survive. It is another example of "survival of the fittest", and of course those stronger genes are, theoretically from an evolutionary perspective the ones that are passed on and ensure survival of the species.

So pathogens are not *bad* unless our immune system is compromised, because we can with many fight many of them off, with or without the help of medicine, in whichever form that medicine comes.

So, in it's own way, it could be argued that the reason pathogens contain Nature's Medicine Code is because they are part of the ecosystem, and part of nature, and so of course *will* contain Nature's Medicine Code by default.

This, of course, only applies to naturally occurring rather than man-made viruses.

There will be differences. I am going to use the analogy of the orchestra one more time.

Bacteria

We all carry bacteria and viruses within and on us. The issue is whether they will make us sick.

We all need some bacteria to be healthy – particularly in the gut, as we have already explored, and will continue to explore.

I have already talked about how bacteria are like the string section of the orchestra. We need them to have a whole, balanced orchestra that can play a beautiful symphony.

We need so-called "good" bacteria for a healthy immune system.

In the orchestra analogy, imagine that a couple of new string players have arrived, and they play pretty badly - completely out of tune in fact. In the context of a whole orchestra, the conductor (immune system) can manage this, and just kicks them out. This would be akin to the immune system overcoming a mild bacterial infection.

Now imagine that the conductor was a little bit distracted when those two players first joined, and then didn't pay enough attention, and before anyone realised, the out of the tune players realised they were onto a good thing with this amazing orchestra and invited all their (equally badly playing) mates to come along. Imagine that these mates are pretty rowdy, so the whole orchestra gets thrown into chaos. Two things might happen:

a)   the conductor realises how serious the issue is, and quickly rushes over and throws them all out.

b)   the conductor calls for reinforcements. Some firm but polite and caring guards show up, who are careful to get to the string players without causing further upset to the rest of the orchestra (like taking a more natural medicine)

c)   the conductor calls for reinforcement but this time massive brutish security guards come charging in, paying absolutely no attention to anything other than getting to the disruptor as quickly as possible, knocking over other musicians at they come hurtling through, and causing their music manuscripts to go flying into the air. This is like what medicines, foods, toiletries and substances that are disharmonious, and don't contain all aspects of Nature's Medicine Code, do.

Of course, sometimes the invasion of all of the out-of-tune string players is so chaotic that the only way of countering the damage is to get the brutish security guards in. But of course, in getting rid of the awful string musicians, they have trashed the rest of the orchestra. So the orchestra - the body - needs rebuilding afterwards in order to play a harmonious symphony again.

Viruses

Now viruses are interesting. Viruses are clever. In the analogy of the orchestra, they are like another conductor coming along whilst the first conductor has popped out for lunch......and then locking the doors so the original conductor can't get back in. Easily, anyway.

As in the case of bacteria, there are viruses that slowly affect a person's health, or for a short period of time, or there are those that can cause severe health problems that could even be fatal.

Let's look at both in terms of the orchestra analogy.

It is in a virus' interests to progress slowly, because it will die when the host dies. So the *really* clever ones take their time so they can live longer.

In the orchestra, this is the new conductor who has arrived and appears with an amazing new manuscript, a wonderful charming winning smile (think Professor Gilderoy Lockhart from Harry Potter). Many of the musicians are so charmed and giddy with delight that they don't realise that there is a problem. The musicians who do go off to look for their original conductor, this might take some time. In the meantime, this new conductor gets most of the musicians to do exactly as he wants them to, and they are happy to do so.

The sceptical musicians however hear banging on a locked door, open it, and let the original conductor in, who tells the new conductor that he either has to leave, to go and sit and watch - but mustn't make a sound or move whilst sitting listening. This is a bit like what the HIV and Epstein-Barr viruses do.

The fast acting and deadlier viruses like ebola are like a new conductor who is arrogant, and doesn't care about being liked. He shouts preposterous claims about how he is better, and how the original conductor is a disgrace to music. The musicians dislike him so much that when he starts conducting, they can't play very well - they don't feel connected to the music, to their instruments, to each other. They miss their original conductor, and don't know what to do. In the end, it becomes impossible for them to play music.

Now dealing with viruses becomes interesting. These new conductors are trained in a specialised form of a martial art, and so aren't really interested in or bothered by the security guards. The new conductor needs a black belt in the same specialised form of a martial art.

The same is true of man-made viruses - the conductors need a black belt in the same specialised form of a martial art.

Antibiotics

Antibiotics kill bacteria, but they kill *all* bacteria - they are unable to discriminate between "good" bacteria and disease-causing pathogens.

In the orchestra, this is where *all* of the string section is destroyed, not just the renegade musicians that can't play. Whilst those musicians have been got rid of, there is a gaping hole in the orchestra with the loss of the great string players too. The orchestra cannot play a proper symphony, the conductor (immune system) fails to keep the orchestra working properly as they don't know how to compensate for their loss. They all struggle.

The orchestra is weak, the conductor desperate. When new string players show up, the conductor can't turn them away, even if they play poorly. We get infections more easily again.

Of course antibiotics are sometimes necessary. Building up the string section with excellent string players - repopulating the gut bacteria is crucial - when taking antibiotics. I was amazed when travelling in India, and at the time needing antibiotics (because I didn't know then how to prevent gut infections, or treat them naturally), I was always given a prescription for probiotics by the doctor, as well as the antibiotics. There are other countries that do this too, which is a leading approach to using Western medicine.

Natural Treatments

What is amazing is that there are plant medicines and homeopathic medicines that have an anti-bacterial and/or anti-viral action in ways that conventional medicines don't have – in that, in the case of bacterial infections, they don't destroy the healthy gut bacteria; they can differentiate because healthy bacteria and disease-causing pathogens.

In the case of these pathogens, I would suggest that the key differential is the harmonious music – there may be *part* of Nature's Medicine Code in the form of Phi and the Golden Spiral present, and so the body might think they are health-giving for a short time – but actually the *sound* generated by the whole orchestra (the whole body) isn't harmonious, and this is how and when the immune system realizes something is wrong and then goes into action. It protects the great string players, but only gets rid of the troublemakers. Harmonious medicines look after the harmonious musicians, disrupting and getting rid of only the disharmonious ones.

Using harmonious medicine is the way forward.

Sonication is a process by which sound frequencies are used to agitate particles – and have been successfully used to break the cell walls of bacteria (and so destroy the bacteria).

Mathematical and Sound Treatments in Allopathic Medicine

Allopathic is another word for conventional medicine, which is turning both to mathematics and sound for help with destroying pathogens.

Sonication for cancer and other diseases is showing positive results – this is the use of high frequency sound (usually ultrasound) as a treatment. In the case of bacteria, the use of sound can break down bacterial cell walls – this causes all of the contents of the bacteria to come spilling out and they die.

Some research is also starting to investigate how to disrupt the perfect mathematical structures of viruses as a way of destroying them – there is now a branch of virology called Mathematical Virology.

A Healthier Immune System

One last point to consider is this.

When the body is naturally exposed to naturally-occurring bacteria and viruses, and has a healthy immune system, the original conductor (who was clever in the first place) will learn how to deal with the rogue musicians, and the opportunistic new conductor – the original conductor will be primed ready to more quickly respond to any future incursion.

That is how our immune system develops when allowed to do so naturally in its own time, without being artificially overstimulated through vaccination.

Having too many rogue musicians and too many opportunistic new conductors to deal with all at the same would overwhelm any conductor, who never has a chance to properly learn to distinguish between the healthy harmonious sounds and the different notes of the different disharmonious players (each pathogen will have its own different sound). The conductor will then be confused and try to get rid of great musicians "just to sure". He will seek to get rid of some of the healthy orchestra, because he never had the chance to work out what was healthy and what wasn't healthy harmonious sound. This is what is happening with auto-immune disorders; the immune system is confused and has gone into overdrive and is attacking the healthier parts of the body.

This is what multiple vaccinations do, and why it is unhelpful to the overall health of the immune system.

When we vaccinate our children young, we never give the immune system – the conductor - the opportunity to hear the whole orchestra play, to hear a beautiful symphony, and to learn the difference between healthy harmonious and unhealthy disharmonious sound. The conductor will forever be struggling to keep up knowing how to conduct because he never learned how to conduct in the first place.

We will come to look at how we can support our health, immune system and a healthy gut in the last section, Part 6: Steps to Health.

Part 4: Medicine and the Mind

It is very important when talking about medicine to also talk about the placebo effect.

I first came across a remarkable scientist called Dr David Hamilton at a talk in early 2009. David has a PhD in pharmacology and worked for Astra Zeneca, a large drug company, doing research into drugs to treat cancer and cardiovascular disease.

He was surprised to find that the placebo effect was often shown to be as powerful as the drugs themselves, sometimes a little more, sometimes a little less, but overall usually had a similar level of success. He tried to explore this with colleagues who just dismissed it as "the placebo effect", and told him to stop thinking about it. Often it is even dismissed when the results of drug trials are made public too, the "placebo" effect results are not included in the published data.

So David left his job at Astra Zeneca, took himself back to his hometown, Glasgow in Scotland, took up a bar job to support himself, and started his own research project, interviewing people who had cured themselves of so-called "incurable diseases" – cancers, diabetes and genetic disorders like myasthenia gravis.

He found that all of the hundreds of people he spoke to – bar a tiny handful – did the same thing. They used the power of thought to cure themselves. They *imagined* – visualized – themselves getting better. They didn't have any biological understanding of what they visualizing in many cases – they just imagined the diseased part of their body getting better.

He gave a extraordinary example of a man in Scotland who had been in a terrible car accident. The car was destroyed, and his body was broken all over. He was told by his consultant that – with intensive rehabilitation – he would get 80% of his movement back after 1 year.

The man replied by telling the consultant that he would run the Glasgow Marathon in a year.

He set to work. He would lay in bed (because it was all he could do) and visualise little "mini-me" construction workers, tiny versions of himself wearing little helmets, going around his body repairing what needed repairing. He imagined construction workers using magic thread to sew up the crack in his skull, and travelling around his body, working and fixing all that needed to be repaired. The mini-me construction workers worked shifts, so when one shift ended, and they went to rest, a new group of mini-me workers would come out for their shift and carry on the good work of their colleagues.

The most amazing evidence of the power of his approach came from what happened to his hip joint. The man had had an arthritic hip from before the accident. This could be clearly seen on the scans that had been taken of him when he was first admitted to hospital. The ball joint in his hip was clearly serrated. So whilst working on the rest of his body, he imagined his little mini-me construction workers using sandpaper to smooth over his hip joint. By the time the final scans were carried out a year later, his previously serrated arthritic hip joint was *smooth*. That was the miraculous improvement in this patient's remarkable recovery that the consultant simply couldn't explain. And of course, he ran the Glasgow Marathon, as he said that he would.

David published an amazing book – *How Your Mind Can Heal Your*

Body – which documented his research.

(As a quick aside, I went away from that talk, totally inspired, and decided I would heal my short-sighted vision. David suggested half an hour every day of visualisation. I get easily distracted sometimes, so I did ten minutes a day for a week then forgot about it. A couple of months later, whilst on holiday in the US, I stood up in the middle of the night to go to the toilet and accidentally trod on my glasses. Now I have worn glasses since I was 8 years old, and they have been mega important in my life so I can *see* and I have *never* broken a pair due to their importance to me. But a thought immediately occurred to me: "my eyes have improved".

The ophthalmologist who then tested my eyesight when I went to get a new pair of glasses was stunned to find that one eye had improved 5% – and the other a whopping 20%. She couldn't believe how it had happened when I explained what I had done. It definitely wasn't because of my developing near-sightedness as I was only 35 years old, and there were no signs of that then. The ophthalmologist was baffled. I of course wasn't).

Anyway, back to the placebo effect. The placebo effect is something we have to stop dismissing. The placebo effect is something to be astonished by and celebrated *because it is the power of the mind to heal our bodies.*

Let me say that again.

We have *consistent* evidence that the mind is *as powerful, sometimes more powerful* than the pharmaceutical drugs that we take. Without side effects. It turns out the mind can be a medicine.

There is another reason it is important to mention the placebo effect in this book. I have talked about different forms of medicine - pharmaceutical drugs, herbal medicines, food and homeopathy. Of all of these, homeopathy has been dismissed the most by those who don't understand it as being "just the placebo effect". For those of us who have used homeopathy with newborn babies and pets, and those who simply cannot be exhibiting a placebo response know it works amazingly. Will there be a placebo effect sometimes? Of course – as with all medicine, or any pharmaceutical drug, there can be a placebo effect because our minds are powerful. The placebo effect is to be respected because it is evidence of the power we have when we put our minds and hearts to good use to bring about positive changes we would like see, including with our health.

And yet, separately to this, there is still plenty of documented evidence of the success people and animals can have using homeopathy that simply cannot be explained by the placebo effect. And – unlike pharmaceutical medicine – it does not cause side effects.

But what does this all mean in terms of the mind?

Given that the mind is clearly a tool for medicine, my final suggestion to add to this Theory of medicine is that

18) The mind can heal the body through a process of visualising and meditating using Nature's Medicine Code; Phi and the Golden Spiral flowing healthily through every part of the body, DNA, and electromagnetic field, along with harmonious sounds, in particular, the Solfeggio frequencies. We are connecting with the power & vibration of love, which heals.

Part 5: Emotional and Mental Wellness & Happiness

Our physical health, as I have already mentioned is connected to our emotional and mental health, and natural medicine practitioners are always interested in what is *happening emotionally* for a person, even when physical symptoms present themselves.

Anything that brings disharmony to the mind will bring disharmony to the body, in fact naturopaths and holistic medicine practitioners are usually interested in what has happened to someone *emotionally* that has led to a physical disease. Louise Hay was the original proponent of the link between emotional and physical health some 20 years ago, and this understanding how become almost mainstream.
It therefore follows that what makes us feel emotionally uncomfortable, can make us physically sick.

Natural medicine practitioners are interested in what was happening in the life of a person, and their emotions, in the time before, or during, the development of a disease. Even seemingly physical conditions will have a mental or emotional connection – a broken leg for example could be because either the person deep down, in their subconscious, needed to slow down (maybe they had been doing too much), or are afraid of moving forward.

The question we ask is "what was going on (emotionally or in the person's life) before or during the development of this disease?"

This is also known as the *aetiology* of a condition – the "Never Been Well Since" (NBWS).

The mind-body connection is a strong one, and Nature's Medicine Code applies just as much here as it does to our physical health, and our use of medicine.

A lack of happiness or mental or emotional health and wellness – anything that brings disharmony to what we think and how we feel – brings disharmony to the body. Our orchestra struggles to play a beautiful symphony when we are sad, as well as when we have a physical illness or are struggling with too many toxins. But ensuring your happiness is probably the best way to strengthen your conductor – a happy conductor will be easily able to inspire the whole orchestra to play that beautiful symphony. An unhappy one will feel overwhelmed and find it hard to inspire and lead, an angry one will just shout at the musicians who will stop playing beautiful rhythmic harmonious sounds.....but a *happy* conductor, who feels fulfilled and joyous can do *anything*. Our immune system is like that. When happy, it can do *anything*.

Happiness is one thing, but what about mental health problems?

With the orchestra analogy, it is what the orchestral choir section – the singers – are up to that affects the harmonious production of a symphony. This is like the mind in the body.

If the orchestral choir section is feeling down, they will complain more, be more sensitive to mistakes, point them out more – like our own limiting self-doubts. This can lead – if unchecked by the conductor – to feelings of helplessness and worthlessness, and a loss of energy and passion because of being overwhelmed by the chaotic sounds. There will be a lack of true harmony in the voices of the singers. The orchestra may even grind slowly to a halt, with musicians feeling miserable looking at their beautiful instruments that they have lost the passion to play. The effect is to make the conductor feel depressed too because the orchestra isn't playing the beautiful symphony it is capable of producing – the immune system becomes weakened.

In psychoses and psychotic experiences such as those that people with schizophrenia and type 1 bipolar affective disorder, the analogy would be that the orchestral choir is singing WAY TOO LOUDLY. And each singer is singing a different song, competing with each other to see who can be the loudest, so it becomes a cacophony of chaotic sound. It's exhausting for the conductor and the rest of the orchestra, and the individual musicians can't hear their own instruments.

There is a total lack of *harmony*. And there is a lack of the feeling of being at peace emotional and mentally.

MRI scans show that brains differ in people with psychoses, and neuroscientists are showing that childhood trauma – disharmony – causes changes to the brain.

If we take the body to be an expression of the perfect mathematical proportions of Phi, and an expression of the Golden Spiral and harmonious sound frequencies, then this will apply to the brain too. So where people have mental illness or whose brains have been affected by trauma, their brain structure will change, and I would suggest that there is a loss of Phi and the Golden Spiral; of harmonious sound vibrations, in the same way that I hypothesised happens with the physical body.

So in this disharmonious situation, what can we do? To add in more disharmony in the form of disharmonious medicine isn't really going to be a long term solution to the orchestra or the conductor that enables them to keep playing. It might create a bigger disharmony that temporarily nullifies the chaotic choir, but the choir needs a lasting way to find their way back to harmony again.

There are newer branches of psychiatric and psychological medicine interested in bringing health and balance to mental health – through therapy, and even more recently nutritional psychiatry and nutritional psychology. A lack of essential nutrients is now known to contribute to the onset of poor mental health, and so using food and supplements to support mental and emotional wellbeing is becoming increasingly popular. In fact there is an organisation called the *International Society for Nutritional Psychiatry Research.*

And, as this Theory suggests, if the nutrition comes from organic *harmonious* foods and supplements, that contain the mathematical properties of Phi, and the geometry of the Golden Spiral, and what the body and mind know to be a *harmony* in terms of sound, then the food will truly be supportive of physical and mental health.

When I was working as a mental health keyworker, I was struck by how the only times everybody's symptoms calmed down naturally, were when they were eating or listening to calming music, which fits with what we have been describing here about the importance of sound and sound vibrations. I was fortunate to always work in places where nutritious meals were an important part of the care and nourishment provided, all of it made in a natural home-made caring way, both contributing to wellness in ways suggested happen in this theory.

Every branch of natural medicine including Traditional Chinese Medicine (TCM), medical herbalism, nutritional therapy and homeopathy includes treatment options for mental wellness and to support mental health, and emotional and mental wellbeing.

We explore in the next part; Part 6: Steps to Health what you can do to support your mental health and emotional wellbeing.

There is no coincidence that this is a theory about the music and mathematics of *harmonia*. A balanced life, where we are at peace with ourselves, accept who we are, accept others, celebrate our strengths – these are all about living a harmonious life by being a person in harmony with oneself. As parents, educators, leaders, teachers, doctors, psychologists, natural medicine practitioners, neighbours, friends, if we seek to support others to find their way to this harmonia – to balance – we support the health of the *whole* person. By valuing and accepting our individual differences and celebrating our weaknesses as well as our strengths, and inspiring others to do the same, then harmony and health will be easier for all.

Ultimately, a harmonious mind creates a harmonious body, and a harmonious mind and body build a harmonious life – and together as harmonious people we can build a harmonious world. So physical *and* mental health combined need be brought into harmony.

Part 6: Steps to a Healthier You

This is where we get practical. So, if it is the case that the body only accepts as healthy medicines, foods and toiletries that are in their natural state of Phi and Golden Spiral geometry and harmonic sound vibrations; or energy medicines that can show the immune system how to return to health, then how can you make simple changes to your life that massively improve your health?

It is one thing to have knowledge, understanding or an intuition on a positive step we can take. It is another thing to actually *take action* to bring about health.

Before I tell you the steps, I am going to share something that I hope helps gives you the courage to take action. It involves sharing an experience I had as a teenager. It goes like this.

My mother was *embarrassing.*

She wasn't your standard "normal" Mum. She was an immigrant from Yugoslavia living in London, England, who couldn't understand normal western ways of living and behaving due to her peasant farming Slavic background. She was already eccentric, but this combination was something I – as a teenage girl with low self-esteem who wanted to blend in and not stand out – found excruciating sometimes. She would ask for "Durex" loudly in her heavy Yugoslav accent in shops when she meant "Duracell", would wear bling gold, and would breathe in front of my friends....you know, the stuff we worry about as teenagers. What made it worse was that she was – well – into *natural* stuff. Like organic food and natural toiletries, which was so *unfashionable.*

This was in the late 1980s, when to get hold of organic food and natural toiletries meant going to one of three shops in London. We drove all the way to Southall in far West London one day in the late 1990s, when my mother read an article about a plant-based range of cleaning products – there wasn't anything like it in existence at the time. We bought it from the *importer* because it wasn't in the shops yet. It is now one of the leading brands of such products in the UK.

My mum's perspectives bothered me. I was a teenage city girl living in trendy London, and used my chemist shop discount to collect one of each of a whole range of cheap body sprays and all sorts of shampoos and conditioners that promised me magic hair. I didn't want to smell *natural*. Being with my mother, that meant smelling of *garlic*, that mega-unfashionable immune system boosting natural antibiotic, and cardiovascular gem. Urgh no. And my mother would *grow her own organic vegetables* in the back garden using *manure*. When she offered me home-grown vegetables, I would in my loving, thoughtful teenage-daughterly way, turn my nose up because I didn't want to eat anything a slug had shared.

It took me a while to realise that my mother was a trend-setting ultra cool genius - some time after she had passed in fact, bless her wise heart. Oh how she laughs from the "other side". She taught me the power of listening to your gut feelings – no matter what anyone else says – and how the consumer choices we make literally can change not just our health, but the health of the world.

When my Mum started out, almost no-one did what I suggest here, and as a consumer, she had very little choice. Everyone (including me) thought she was mad because what she was doing was different to what everyone else was doing – she wasn't following the "norm".

When I started to follow in her footsteps more than a decade later, there was a lot more choice, but still my choices were not the norm.

Now, for most people in the developed world, the steps I suggest below are relatively easy to follow because the range of choices available to consumers is vast, and growing by the day – it is cool and forward thinking in today's day and age to take action that supports your health, the health of your loved ones and the planet.

Taking action in these ways benefits us in three ways:

1) Our health will improve (and with that we will have more energy and feel more positive, which can only positively impact on our careers, happiness and relationships)

2) We will inspire others to do the same, and so support better health for the people we love, and they in turn will have a more positive impact on the people around them as well as the planet

3) We will bring change to health providers, food producers and manufacturers because how we spend our money is literally a vote for how we want the world to be. Companies have seen the explosion in the demand for organic foods and natural toiletries, and they want your money, so there are more and more options that they are providing. The thing is, often what is sold as "pure" and "natural" isn't, and I provide a guide in this chapter to how to understand what the labels *REALLY* mean, and to make choices that really do support your health, rather than falsely claim to.

In the following pages, I share what you can do to bring Nature's Medicine Code into every aspect of your life.

To help you make choices that support your health, your family's health and the health of the planet, I have explained *how* a lot of the products we use in our everyday lives cause health problems. You knowing what they do gives you power and choice in every part of your life.

Inherent in what I share is the theory that Nature's Medicine Code – Phi and the Golden Spiral, Solfeggio frequencies and Schumann waves – cannot be found in the synthetic chemicals used in many every products, but are found in natural products.

You will also a few of my suggestions about what I have found from years of trialling and testing different products to find the best I could find. I am not paid by any of the companies I mention, these are my honest recommendations based on years of trialling and testing what I think is the best.

To know *why* these changes are necessary, I have explained the reasons you need to make the switch. To me, this isn't about giving you reasons to be afraid of what we are exposed to, it's about helping you realise how *powerful* you are when you make a choice to live differently. When you, and your family, and then your friends, as well as me and all of mine do that, businesses follow suit as they want our money. Knowledge really is power.

So see your money as your way of voting for what you want to see more of in the world – and use it only for things that bring you health. In the process, you will change how companies behave and what they produce. And you'll be cool. Because these things have become cool. You get to Be The Change. How great is that going to make you feel?

Steps to Health

We are fortunate to live in a time where we can access information at any time, anywhere, at the tips of our fingers. Everything I share here is what I have come to learn over a 30 year period. I am not a doctor, or a pharmacist, or a nutritionist.

Please don't take my word for any suggestions I make. Please do your own research and find all of this out for yourself – my greatest wish is that you become your own researcher, to learn to find the truth about what you are taking, eating and using, so that you can make consumer and health choices with greater knowledge and understanding for you and your loved ones.

Having said that, please remember that you are 100% fully accountable for and responsible for any decisions you make regarding your health, and you must always consult with your doctor about any changes to medication you are being prescribed, or because of any health concerns or issues that you might have.

1) Healthcare

Most people who choose to work as healthcare professionals do so because they care about people and people's health. However, in most cases, conventionally trained health professionals have studied health using a limited curriculum that has been written by the pharmaceutical industry which does not include holistic whole-body systems thinking, or an understanding of the science that recognises that we are 99% energy, or more than a cursory introduction to nutrition.

It's important to respect the work of all health workers, even when we make alternative healthcare choices. There is a place for conventional medicine for all of us. When we need emergency help, for example, what paramedics, doctors and nurses do is remarkable.

However pharmaceutical drugs aren't the only option for treating health conditions. There are many other options that don't cause serious side effects or put pressure on the immune system or the rest of the body.

Of course, as I have said above, you are 100% fully accountable for and responsible for any decisions you take regarding your health, and you must always consult with your doctor about any changes to medication you are being prescribed, or if you have any concerns about your health.

You may also want to explore any of the following options.

- Register with a qualified naturopath, homeopath and/or nutritionist to support your health. Some medically trained doctors, midwives, pharmacists are also trained homeopaths or naturopaths. Do your research and find someone that you feel you can trust.

- Use therapies designed to promote your wellbeing that have no side effects when used by qualified, trained practitioners. Reflexology, massage, osteopathy, cranial-sacral therapy, energy healing, sound healing can all make significant improvements to how you feel in your mind and body and improve your health overall.

- If you are on a limited income, many colleges of natural medicine run low cost student clinics where students are supervised by experienced practitioners. Or maybe a member of your family, or a family friend can help with the costs of treatment. Crowdfunding is also used by many many people to raise money for healthcare costs.

- Read the Patient Information Leaflets that comes with any prescribed medication. These are also available online. Each possible side-effect has been reported by a patient who has had an adverse reaction, or has been reported by their carers. Very few people ever report side effects through the proper channels, so you are only reading the tip of the iceberg in terms of the numbers of people affected. Make informed choices about the medication you take.

- Research is showing that walking barefoot in nature reduces inflammatory responses in the body. Touching nature – plants, trees and earth for a reasonable length of time – can have the same effect. So walk barefoot outdoors when the weather allows and hug a tree.

- We pee out the drugs we take, and they go into the water supply. In 2017, one US study found 118 pharmaceuticals in drinking water samples from 25 US treatment plants. If we all reduce the amount of pharmaceutical drugs we take, then other people will be drinking less pharmaceutical drugs through their water supply in built up cities. Pharmaceutical and water companies will claim that the levels are too low to affect human health, however even the smallest traces of medicine can have an effect, when we apply the science of atom, energy and homeopathic principles – and these build up in the environment over time. Furthermore, they aren't rendered harmless once they have been peed out, and affect animals and fish in the environment.

- Explore alternatives to the contraceptive pill in ways that are responsible, where you take full accountability of your sexual health and the sexual health of others. The body, as we have been exploring, has its own natural flow and rhythm, and to interrupt or block that flow and balance, will have a knock-on effect elsewhere in your body in short- and long-term ways.

- Also explore natural alternatives to HRT. The menopause is a natural transition for women to make – not an illness. It is in our elder years that women find the freedom from caring what others think enough to speak up and advocate for others, and share our wisdom. Our centre of power moves from our sacrum (reproductive organs) to our throats (and the energy centre moving up generates rushes of heat). If we haven't processed our trauma, and use alcohol and sugar which throws our hormones out, then our trauma will come up. It's like nature's way of saying "right, you're here to now share all the wisdom you've acquired but you can't do it if you haven't worked through your stuff. So come on now, let's get it done so you can shine in all your powerful awesomeness". HRT just adds synthetic hormones to the environment, to the drinking water our kids drink, whilst blocking the process of us fully actualising our powerful voices (that we could use to bring change......an end to the patriarchy even!)

- Only take antibiotics if 100% absolutely necessary. At the first sign of a possible infection, speak to a naturopathic doctor, as there are natural alternatives to antibiotics including herbal and homeopathic remedies that do not destroy the healthy gut bacteria, and so support the immune system, as well as supplements and essential oils. Save antibiotics for only really serious situations as much as possible.

Speak to your naturopathic practitioner or homeopath about what you can keep in your medicine cupboard to support first aid and family health.

I am not advising or suggesting that you do what I do, as you are responsible for your own health and your family's health, but I am sharing what I keep in mine.

- pure organic lavender oil for cuts and burns - it's naturally anti-inflammatory, antiseptic and cooling.

- I also always keep in my cupboard bottles of organic herbal tinctures:

  Echinacea (boosts white blood cell count, so supports the body when fighting infections)
  Thyme (antibacterial – I use it for stomach bugs and chesty colds) and Elderberry (anti-viral)
  Olive leaf extract is another great anti-viral and anti-bacterial remedy
  Elderberry is a great winter anti-viral immune system booster

- I keep a good homeopathic first aid kid at home, I have a "top-20" favourite remedies I use, with remedies for everything from fevers, to conjunctivitis, splinters, flus, colds, headaches, bumps, bruises, shock, upset stomachs, even burns. I took me a couple of years to start using the remedies, and once I started I wished I hadn't waited so long!

- Zinc and Vitamin C to boost the immune system.

- Vitamin D has been consistently shown in trials to be more effective than the flu vaccination. In fact, low levels of vitamin D makes us more prone to colds and flu, research is finding. The best way to get vitamin D is from the sun (read the section on sunscreens though) if possible, if not supplements are great for overall health.

- Magnesium is another supplement that most people need; it is found in low levels in our soil, and so most people need extra. It is required for many processes in the body – including healthy skin, hair, nails, happier moods, better mental health and better sleep.

• What I now share here on vaccination, I share as someone with vaccine damage, which I have, so I have done a huge amount of research into it.

Objectively look into vaccination, and all of the arguments for why people do and do not vaccinate.

Whatever your perspective, it is a fact that unfortunately there are no adequate safety studies in adults or children for any vaccines. Many doctors, pediatricians, pharmacists, and other health professionals who have looked into the data that is available (and that hasn't been falsified) are choosing to either not vaccinate or use a different vaccine schedule.

There are also almost no studies that compare vaccinated with unvaccinated children. One recent study conducted by Danish scientists with African children did find that children who received the DTaP (diphtheria, tetanus and pertussis) vaccine were *five times more likely to die* in the two months following vaccination than those who hadn't been vaccinated.

Allergies and auto-immune disorders are common longer-term consequences of vaccination, but there are many many serious illnesses, disorders and side effects that you will find listed in the Patient Information Leaflets that can and do happen that affect the cognition, brain function, brain development, neurology, immunity, and hormonal health of the body. As has already been mentioned, very few people report adverse reactions, so the possible side-effects listed represent the tiny tip of a very big iceberg in terms of the numbers affected.

I offer this as someone with vaccine damage. I have an auto-immune disorder that developed over time, following travel vaccines I had in 2005. It took 12 years to realise what my different seemingly disconnected symptoms were. I just didn't think the symptoms were linked, and some were painful and debilitating. I am successfully treating the disorder and manage my health using homeopathy and diet, but I found I have a gene for an auto-immune disorder that some geneticists think suggests those people who have it shouldn't be vaccinated, as the disorder is likely to be triggered. It turns out this gene is common in the Caucasian population. Anyone with any auto-immune diseases in the family should definitely do their research before vaccines are given to their children, as vaccination can lead to the expression of the diseases.

Also, we think side effects show up immediately, but many side effects can take months and years to develop, so people don't think to question vaccines that they might have had many years ago. There are currently questions for example about the exposure to aluminium and heavy metals in vaccines, and in air pollution and the exponential rise in dementia and Alzheimer's. Older people used to still be able to think and live much more easily than they do now. Others are also questioning whether there could be a link with the pressure placed on the immune system by multiple vaccines and the exponential rise in cancers we are seeing, including in children.

There are some big myths told about the benefits of vaccination to individuals and communities to ensure maximum compliance, so be informed, and do read about these. Dr Tetyana Obukhanych is a Harvard Immunologist who provides some interesting perspectives on these myths, including the myth about herd immunity. Herd immunity is impossible to achieve due to the numbers of people whose bodies do not take up the vaccines they are given. Another myth is that vaccination prevents an individual from having a particular disease, but vaccination is not a guarantee. The outbreaks of mumps across campuses in the US in 2016, including Harvard, where 42 students developed the illness, affected only students who had been vaccinated.

A documentary series *The Truth About Vaccines,* which interviews over 60 doctors and medicine professionals, and looks at the history of vaccine development is also a great watch. Edward Jenner, the founder of vaccination, for example, was actually responsible for spreading smallpox, and there was a popular revolt that ended compulsory vaccination because ordinary people worked out those who had been vaccinated by being injected with the pus from smallpox blisters were the ones dying. Smallpox was actually eradicated with the simple step of improving hygiene and sanitation, not vaccination.

This is even more important now with the newer vaccines.

So please do your own research, with an open mind. There is plenty of information available to those willing to look at it all perspectives, and willing to ask questions.

- You may wish to detoxify from vaccinations you have had in the past. You may have been injected with mercury, aluminium, monosodium glutamate, formaldehyde and other toxic heavy metals and preservatives that may need to be cleared from your body for your immune system to function well. There are some expensive heavy metals detox programs, however some simple steps can be taken by speaking to your naturopath, homeopath or nutritionist. Coriander / cilantro is a useful heavy metals detoxifying food.

- CBD (cannabidiol) oil is a wonder medicine, and has improved health outcomes for people with cancers, auto-immune disorders, MS, epilepsy, Parkinson's disease, Alzheimer's, anxiety, depression, pain, inflammation, psychoses, schizophrenia, PTSD, diabetes, antibiotic-resistant infections and cardiovascular disease amongst others. It works on the body's Endocanabinoid System, which some are arguing is the most important system in establishing and maintaining health. It is a system that supports homeostasis – balance – in the body.

It needs to be organic and grown naturally – as Nature's Medicine Code suggests. There are a lot of products on the market, do research which ones are the best, as some really are better quality than others and contain more of all of the whole plant extract. Some are just selling hemp oil – however what is needed is whole plant CBD oil. As I discussed in the Theory, I would suggest that it contains all 6 Solfeggio frequencies and is a truly incredible medicine.

Diet & Nutrition

Doctors famously make the Hippocratic Oath, which is a set of principles of medical ethics first developed by Hippocrates, a 5th century doctor, who is seen as the father of Western medicine. Whilst it is debated whether there is truly evidence that Hippocrates also said: "Let food be thy medicine and medicine be thy food", the fact is that this quote (whoever first said it) couldn't be more true.

All our food is there to make energy in our bodies – literally to make something called ATP (adenosine triphosphate) in the mitochondria (energy making magic machines) in our cells. So the food must be healthy, and life – energy – giving to help us be well.

1) Go organic. It goes without saying that eating a healthy diet is important, but many foods have medicinal properties, but you will only have the medicinal effect if the food is organic (in particular free from pesticides, herbicides and GMOs).

   This Theory suggests that the body doesn't recognise the codes of pesticides and herbicides as being those of health, and so even if the fruit or vegetable they are sprayed upon is healthy, the body will go into immune response alert because it can't get to the goodness as it's covered in codes that mean "foreign object; quick! Get rid of it!".

   Organic is important. We know that Glyphosate, the main ingredient in Roundup weedkiller, and the main weedkiller used around the world, causes cancer, as confirmed in 2015 by the WHO's International Agency for Research on Cancer (IARC).

   What does it do and how does it work? Kate Birch's excellent book *Glyphosate Free* describes in detail how glyphosate works in the body.

   Firstly, it is not just a weedkiller, it is also an antibiotic, so continually challenging the health of our gut. It also competes with a crucial amino acid we need in the body – glycine. So receptors for glycine get taken up with glyphosate, and there is no room for glycine in those receptors.

Glycine is needed for the production of an enzyme that enables us to digest gluten, other processes that produce vitamin B9 needed for heart, respiratory and nervous system health, mitochondrial function and ATP production, endocrine function including the production of serotonin, melatonin and dopamine and detoxification processes in the body.

Glyphosate stops glycine being able to do it's work, and so affects all of these processes. In other words, glyphosate interferes with our body's heart, respiration, nervous system function, energy levels, hormonal function, affects the production of serotonin, melatonin and dopamine, damages the immune system and makes detoxification more difficult.

Biotech industry funded research claims that it does not bioaccumulate, and that there are "safe levels", but this is untrue. A crowdfunded truly independent study in 2016 proved that glyphosate does indeed bioaccumulate. So there are no safe levels of it.

Many free from foods are marketed as healthy however free from is NOT free from if it is full of pesticides. It can be, vegan, gluten free, refined sugar free etc but if it is made with toxic pesticides, it's not healthy. It is ONLY truly free from if it is organic too.

Your green smoothie is a toxic wasteland if it isn't organic, so make the switch.

Write to companies who make your non-organic "free from" favourites and tell them you want them to be organic and why.

Think it is expensive? Modern food production methods have pushed down prices, so we think food should be cheap – but growing good food can't be done cheaply. After the Second World War, we budgeted a third of our incomes for housing, a third for bills, clothes and going out, and a third for food – because we knew back then it takes money to grow good food.

Think the standards are slipping or dubious? Organic standards are not the same around the world, some standards are questionable. However if we all buy food with a message that says "we want food free from these chemicals", we will collectively as consumers make it easier to push for better standards.

And there is one final consideration.

Many of the pesticides, herbicides and GMOs are made by companies who either invest in war, or in the case of Monsanto, directly produce chemicals that are used as agents of war. Monsanto sold White Phosphorus, a substance that burns and sticks to the skin, and has been used on people in Gaza as recently as 2017, as well as having produced Agent Orange.

When we buy non-organic food, we are supporting companies that directly and indirectly may be supporting war, and the awful damage we see happening to innocent men, women and children in the world.

The food you eat may be killing innocent people. Literally.

We can change that. Starve those companies of the money they need by choosing only organic / pesticide / herbicide and GMO free.

2) Meat & dairy

Meat often comes from animals with cancer, but the cancerous tumours get cut out before the meat is sold on the shelves in your supermarket. In the US, and in the European Union, cattle is fed GMO foods, so GMOs get into your body via meat that is not organic.

Processed meat is a Class 1 Carcinogen, as listed by the U.S.'s FDA (Food & Drugs Administration). A Harvard study by Dr Ganmaa Davaasambuu and her colleagues found pasteurized factory milk to contain up to 33 times more estrone sulfate – an oestrogen compound linked to testicular, prostate and breast cancers.

Conventional meat is full of antibiotics, vaccines, growth hormones, GMOs and other veterinary drugs that don't contain Nature's Medicine Code.

Milk contains pus and antibiotics, vaccines, growth hormones and other veterinary drugs that don't contain Nature's Medicine Code, but also - at least in milk from non-organic dairies - the energy and emotion of sorrow, of mothers and babies who have been separated. Do you really want to drink a milk filled with the sorrow of a mother whose calf has been forcibly taken from her? If you would like to consume milk and dairy products, choose organic farms that use sustainable farming practices that keep calves and mothers together, and doesn't over-milk the mothers.

3) Avoid fast foods and fizzy drinks. They are processed with and made with chemicals that – you guessed it – trigger an immune response in the body.

4) Use only organic cold-pressed oils for cooking. Most standard oils are extracted from the plants, fruits and vegetables using synthetic chemical solvents that this theory suggests the body will read as "foreign objects" and trigger an immune response.

5) Stop eating everyday wheat. Wheat strains we now eat were genetically modified at a time when experiments were first begun, and bear no resemblance to the strains of wheat our ancestors grew. Our bodies don't like today's genetically altered strains. Also, it used to be that the time taken to transform wheat from a grain being harvested in the field to flour in a bag would be weeks. Now it is 24-48 hours in most cases, and this means that we aren't getting the whole wheat in a way that our bodies can more easily process.

Organic sourdough breads are made in such a way that the fermentation process breaks down gluten. Some people find it easier to digest because of this.

Many free from breads are full of additives that make them very difficult for the body to digest. One brand in particular makes healthy looking wraps that.........don't decompose once opened for *weeks*. I know. I have tested them. If food doesn't decompose naturally, it won't decompose in your body either.

6) Avoid eating cane sugar. Some studies show that cane sugar can lower the body's immunity for up to 5 hours after it has been eaten, and other research shows it is more addictive than cocaine (some say five times more, one study says eight times more addictive than cocaine). In fact, eating sugar prevents the body's natural healing processes – because it is using so much energy to deal with the sugar.

Also, zero-sugar or low-sugar products usually contain chemically synthetic sweeteners that consistent studies have shown cause a multitude of health problems in the laboratory, including liver cancer in rats. Due to the introduction of the "sugar tax" in the UK, many companies are renaming artificial sweeteners, or introducing new ones, including major chocolate brands. Read the labels – anything that has been trademarked, or branded as a sweetener will have been chemically made, if you haven't heard of it, it may be new and one to avoid.

Use alternative natural sweeteners instead like organic fruits, dates and maple syrup. Coconut sugar and dark agave syrup do not have the same impact on the body that cane sugar does and are a better alternative although they are processed. Fruits, dates and maple syrup are the best option because they are unprocessed.

7) Research what you need to eat to live a balanced diet. This is one of the most fundamental ways in which you can keep your immune system healthy. A good rule of thumb is organic, 60% raw, no wheat, gluten, cane sugar or processed foods as much as you possibly can.

8) There are some vegetarian and vegan alternative foods that are grown artificially in laboratories, there is one particularly popular brand in the UK. A Chinese doctor once explained to me that according to Chinese Medicine, the body doesn't recognise that substance as food, and doesn't know what to do with it, so sees it as a foreign object and then the immune system tries to get rid of it. Many plant-based burgers contain ingredients that are questionable for health, and are highly processed. I would suggest that these foods don't contain Nature's Medicine Code or the Golden Spiral or harmonious sound vibrations. Avoid them.

9) Follow changes in labelling descriptions. For example GMO has been relabelled "bio fortified", or "nature identical". Aspartame has been relabelled "Sucralose".

10) 3D printing of food - especially meat has begun. As has growing food containing vaccines. Eating food that you know has been grown organically, in nature, is becoming increasingly important - or, indeed, growing your own.

11) Look after your gut bacteria. There are different estimates of the level of importance that a healthy gut has to a healthy immune system, but it is generally agreed that 80% of your immune system is linked to a healthy gut. We also produce most of our serotonin (our happy neurotransmitter) in our gut, so a healthy gut helps us have a healthy mind and immune system. You can do the following:

- Drink kombucha / water-based kefir and eating raw fermented vegetables helps to repopulate the gut bacteria.

- Take a good quality probiotic.

- Drink filtered water that doesn't contain chlorine (tap water is usually chlorinated) – drinking chlorine can destroy gut bacteria.

- Go swimming in non-chlorinated swimming pools, or in natural swimming pools (drinking chlorinated swimming pool water really isn't great for gut health).

- Avoid processed sugar, and limit how much yeast and wheat you eat.

- Eat whole unprocessed foods.

- Aloe Vera juice (organic) is a wonderful soothing drink that supports the whole digestive system – and is cooling and anti-inflammatory for the whole body.

- Mastic Gum (Mastiha) is an amazing resin that comes from trees that grow on the Greek island of Chios. Mastic Gum has been proven to destroy Helicobacter pylori, and other pathogens in the digestive system including parasites, is anti-inflammatory, and has been shown in-vitro to have anti-cancer properties and to work with inflammatory bowel disorders.

- Colonic irrigation can help flush out undigested waste and pathogens.

- Faecal transplants have started being used as a way of obtaining healthy gut bacteria, and are transforming the lives of some of the people who have them, including people with auto-immune conditions.

10) Fasting is showing positive effects in terms of overall health. We don't need to eat as much as we do, and giving the body time to fast gives it time to bring itself back into balance. A really useful one is the 16/8 daily fast – fasting for 16 hours (eg. 9pm at night – 1pm the following day), just drinking water and herbal teas during the fasting time. Do explore all of the options to find the right one for you.

11) We need fat. The beautiful walls that surround our cells need fat to help them send necessary contents out of the cell, and to receive important nutrients into the cell. Fats are needed for communication between cells, so that our bodies work.

Think fat leads to cholesterol? Think again. The body *makes most of its cholesterol* – it doesn't come from food; and the reason the body makes cholesterol is because of *stress.* The body needs more cholesterol when stressed because it helps it make more cortisol, to help it cope with stress. So eat "good fats" like organic coconut oil, avocados, nuts and seeds, which our bodies know how to break down and pass through, and be serious about reducing your levels of stress.

12) Cook with organic herbs and spices – these are medicinal. Plant medicines (also known as herbal medicines) are made from.......herbs! The clue is in the name! The traditional medicine of India, Ayurveda, uses spices and herbs medicinally too. When people are sick, they are literally made a rice dish containing the fresh spices and herbs they need to make them well again. A true "food is medicine" approach.

It can be difficult to get hold of fresh organic herbs and spices, but these can be easily grown using organic seeds planted in pots on your kitchen window sill.

- Vanillin in vanilla has been shown in laboratory tests on rats to reduce breast, colon and lung cancer cells, as well as being antimicrobial.

- Cinnamon, similarly, has been shown also to have anti-mutagenic effects – in other words, to prevent mutations in cells that can show up as cancers.

- Turmeric is an amazing anti-inflammatory, antibacterial and helps to inhibit the growth of cancers. Make a simple daal to eat with rice, or drink a daily turmeric latte. To do this: make a paste with 3 tbsp turmeric (fresh or powder), 3 tbsp ginger (fresh or powder), 1 tbsp cinnamon (fresh or powder) , a hint of black pepper and a little bit of water. Add 1 tbsp of the paste to a cup of warmed organic almond milk (Rude Health gives the best flavor, doesn't contain preservatives and unnecessary additives, as many dairy-free milks do, and doesn't need additional natural sweeteners).

The other amazing thing about turmeric is that it whitens teeth!! So it may stain everything it touches, but it will whiten your teeth over time. You can put a little bit of powder on your toothbrush, after brushing your teeth and brush it into your gums – it's great for soothing inflamed gums, and I have headed off a potential tooth infection more than once by doing this at the first sign of dental pain or inflamed gums.

- Cardamoms and aniseed are a great digestive aid.

- Thyme for example, is antibacterial and antiviral, and great for colds and flu.

- Parsley is great for alkalizing the body (as is lemon water) – so useful where there is too much acid in the body, in conditions ranging from digestive issues, to inflammation, to cancer. Really great for the liver and as part of any detox regime too.

- Coriander is most well-known for its powerful heavy-metal detoxifying properties, so it is really useful for supporting the liver, and dealing with environmental pollution, and heavy metals from vaccines and other sources. Always use organic, as otherwise your body will be dealing with pesticides while at the same time trying to get the benefits of this great herb.

- Oregano is known as a powerful antibacterial herb, that supports the digestive system.

- Rosemary is another powerful antibacterial herb.

- Sage is useful for fighting fungal infections, and is a great all round cleanser and detoxifier.

- I make a really simple rice dish, with a lovely blend of parsley, sage, rosemary, thyme and oregano, and sprinkle it liberally over some cooked rice, frying in coconut oil with some red onion, courgette, chopped green beans and broccoli, seasoned with Himalayan salt. It tastes fantastic and a great digestive and immune system boosting meal. All organic, of course.

- Nettles are one of the richest sources of minerals we can get, so a nettle tea a day is a great way of getting in calcium, potassium, phosphorus, magnesium, and traces of iron, sodium and zinc. Useful for eczema as it is an astringent.

- Lavender, as I have mentioned, is anti-pyretic (cooling), anti-inflammatory and antiseptic. I use lavender tea for fevers, and lavender is great to add to healthy cake recipes (wheat, dairy and cane sugar free recipes – they can be done, and be made delicious...... I bake a lovely organic, vegan free-from blueberry and lavender cake.

- Dandelion, burdock root and cleavers are amazing blood cleansers and detoxifiers, so great for any inflammatory disorders, liver and kidney problems, acidity, and dandelion has anti-cancer properties. Interestingly dandelion is considered to be a weed – many of the weeds we find in our gardens are actually medicines.

- Celery is another great addition to your diet. Anthony William, in his book *Medical Medium* recommends drinking 400ml of freshly juiced organic celery juice first thing every morning as the best way to detoxify your whole body.

    Wise old herbalists would say that the weeds that grow in *your* garden are most specifically the ones *you* need for your health – as though nature is giving your medicine, based on what it knows you need.

13) Biodynamic food is food that has been planted, cared for, grown and harvested according to the position of different planets, including the moon, as a way of ensuring the maximum amount of water, and nutrient absorption through the soil. Biodynamic farming has a perfect balance of plants, flowers, vegetables and animals on a farm to ensure a complete ecosystem that is in balance with itself in order to ensure the most nutritious outcomes in the food that is grown.

Sound far-fetched? There are two things to consider here. You know that 3pm slump you have where you'd rather have a nap? At 3am and 3pm, no matter where you are in the world, the moon will be the furthest away from the Earth at those times. The moon influences the flow of water – in terms of the tides of the seas – but also in your body. At 3pm, the moon is furthest away, has the least influence over the 80% water we are, and so water flow slows down in our bodies, nutrients and oxygen travel more slowly to where they need to go – and we have a slump. So if the moon is exerting an effect of us, then it will do so on the crops we grow, so harvesting them at times that ensure maximum water content sounds sensible. And if the moon is having that effect on us and the crops we grow, then it also makes sense that the other planets spiraling through the solar system in the Golden Spiral are also having an effect too, even if we haven't easily been able to measure those effects yet.

Biodynamic farming sounds like Nature's Medicine Code applied to farming, and biodynamic food, if you are able to obtain it, will be of beneficial effect to you.

14) Drink filtered water. In addition to the presence of pharmaceutical drugs in tap water mentioned in the Healthcare section, recreational drugs can also be found in tap water. A 2014 study by the Drinking Water Inspectorate in the UK found samples containing benzoylecgonine, a form of cocaine that appears once it has passed through the body which is what urine-based cocaine tests test for. Even though the levels are said to be very very small, as discussed in the second chapter, even small tiny amounts of a substance can have an effect on health and cause a response in the body.

15) Read the ingredients lists on the food you buy. I know it takes time, but I am always amazed at how surprised people I meet are when they read what is in their food – they are always shocked and horrified. Lots of "health foods" and "free from" foods are really full of additives. Xanthan gum, for example, is found in cakes and gluten free breads. Do you know what it is? You know those black spots on broccoli and cauliflower when it is going old? That sticky substance is the basis of xanthan gum. Knowing what you are eating means you are *informed*. It gives you a choice. That choice makes you powerful as a human being, and as a consumer.

In fact, as well as buying organic and 100% natural products as a result of reading this book, the *very best thing you can do is to:*

You are likely to be shocked and horrified a lot of time. That is a good thing. We need to be aware of what we are putting in our bodies and the bodies of your loved ones. Do a search on the ingredients you find listed, with the word "toxic" in the search bar, and be surprised at what you will find. You then can make informed choices for you and your loved ones that are based on loving your body and health – and theirs too.

"Choice is your greatest power. It is an even greater power than love, because you must first choose to be a loving person."

~ Caroline Myss

Supplements

Organic food source supplements are made from foods and so contain Nature's Medicine Code. Most supplements are chemically derived or synthetic, and so don't. If it's cheap, it's unlikely to be a food source supplement. Also watch out for labels that say "made with food source ingredients" – if it isn't made with 100% food source ingredients, some ingredients might be chemical, some might be food source. It's a clever marketing way of hiding chemical fillers and additives.

Toiletries & Cosmetics

Did you know that your skin is the largest organ of your body? Your skin will absorb the chemicals you put on it through its pores, and take them into the bloodstream. At least when we eat chemicals, enzymes in your saliva, and stomach help to break down some chemicals, but this isn't an option when what we put on our skin – the largest organ of the body – is absorbed straight into the bloodstream.

Many synthetic chemicals are linked to a range of serious health problems, including cancers, hormonal problems, neurological and developmental disorders, inflammatory diseases, kidney and liver problems. Some of those chemicals are what are called "petrochemicals"; synthetic chemicals made using petroleum, that well known carcinogen.

Some of these chemicals are now being called "forever chemicals" - a large chemical family of over 10,000 highly persistent chemicals that don't occur in nature. Made of PFAS (per- and polyfluorinated alkyl substances), they are found in food packaging, including pizza boxes, food wrappers, take away boxes, Teflon, firefighting foam, carpets, rugs, furniture textiles, car seats, stain-proof and waterproof clothing, outdoor clothing, umbrellas, menstrual underwear, some cosmetics and make up including some mascaras and foundation, dental floss, astro turf, medical equipment and masks, building products and more.

Even very small doses of PFAS can contribute to different cancers, liver problems and immune system disorders. Most people have PFAS in their blood.

Let me just mention Van Jones, a well known attorney and activist in the U.S. He delivered a speech at the North Dakota Oil Pipeline protests where he said:

"This is as simple as I can say it: water is life, oil is death. Water is life, oil is death. That's not hyperbole. What is oil? Oil is some stuff that's been dead for millions and millions of years. Oil has been dead for 60 million years. Coal has been dead for 150 million years.

Somebody's gotta brainstorm to go and dig up a bunch of dead stuff and then burn it. Burn it in their engines, burn it in their power plants. And then they're shocked. They're shocked that having pulled death out of the ground, we now have death in the lungs of our children in the form of asthma. And we now have death on our oceans in the form of oil spills. And we now have death in the skies in form of climate chaos. What did you think was gonna happen when you started digging up all this death? What did you think was gonna happen?

So we stand for life. Let's power a new civilization based on a living sun, based on the living wind, based on the living imagination of our children and based on the cleanliness, and the purity, and the sacredness of our water."

The same can be said of how we use chemicals made from petroleum ("dead stuff") on our skin. These are just a small selection below, to give you an idea of what they are and what they are capable of doing.

Parabens, for example, are petrochemicals now well known to mimic estrogen. They are a preservative used not just in cosmetics, creams, shaving gels and antiperspirants. Some would say that the estrogenic effect is weak, however in combination with other hormone disrupting chemicals could build up the risk. Whilst a debate about whether they cause cancer has been ongoing or over a decade, they have been found in the breast cancer tissue of women with breast cancer. Breast cancers require higher levels of estrogen to grow.

Dibutylphthalate is a phthalate that helps skin care to be absorbed by the skin, yet is recognized a "probable human carcinogen" by the US' Environmental Protection Agency, yet continues to be widely used by most high street cosmetic producers.

Sodium Lauryl Sulfate (SLS) is a foaming agent added in large quantities (usually the first ingredient listed) to make your cleansing product feel as though its foam is making you clean.

Polyethylene Glycol (PEG) are moisturisers, stabilisers and solvents that make a more consistent product. It is found in moisturisers, creams, cleansers and lots of baby products. They are often contaminated with pollutants including ethylene oxide, dioxane, polycyclic aromatic compounds and heavy metals including arsenic, cadmium, lead, nickel, cobalt and iron. This increases skin permeability and allows pollutants to enter the body through the skin's surface. Dermatitis and irritation are common effects of PEGs. The contaminants often found in PEGs are known carcinogens. Specifically, they have been linked to breast cancer, leukaemia, brain and nervous system cancer, bladder cancer, stomach cancer and pancreatic cancer, as well as Hodgkin's disease. They have been proven to interfere with development, especially the nervous system, and may cause kidney and liver organ toxicity.

This is particularly concerning given that a 2004 study found more than 200 chemicals such as these in the umbilical cords of babies. So with us ingesting these chemicals through our skin, and furniture (see furniture later), what environment are we creating for our babies that will be affecting their development? And what are they drinking in our breast milk?

Just because a product has the words "natural", "plant-based". "non-toxic", or "pure" on it, it doesn't mean that it actually is 100% natural. Those words are used by clever marketing people designed to make you think that you are using a product that is better for your health. In my experience, nothing could be further from the truth – and even some products in health or wholefoods shops are not 100% natural, so this is where learning to read the ingredients (and understand and decipher clever marketing) gives you choice and power in choosing only products that do not damage your health, or the health of the people around you who are exposed to it, or the babies you carry in your belly, or the fish and sea-life that have to ingest the chemicals that come out in your pee.

Also, watch out for more clever marketing tricks such as one well-known brand, Original Source, at the time of writing puts

100% natural

fragrance

on its labels. Did you see that? So the *fragrance* (the teeny little word you probably didn't see) is 100% natural, but the product still contains synthetic chemicals. You wouldn't think the product isn't 100% natural because you are so happy seeing enlarged words.

Marketing people are clever. Be cleverer. Read the small print.

The best way you can tell is using *your nose* - but only after a complete detox of synthetic chemicals in your home and personal life for around 6 weeks, your sense of smell and taste will return to normal, as it won't be clogged up with nasties anymore that have been de-sensitising you.....and you will be able to *smell* artificial chemicals yourself, and become your own barometer.

It is important to do a 100% detox though to give the senses a chance to kick back into action. It can be done – I like many others have done it (despite my love or perfumes and body sprays from my days of working in a chemist).

My favourite company for great quality hair products in the UK is Green People. They are expensive, but so concentrated that you only need a tiny amount and they last for ages.

Skincare products: Essential Blends by Sophie Joseph are amazing, and my absolute favourite.

Petroleum Jelly – a Special Case

We think that reaching out for our tub of Vaseline or aqueous cream is just the best thing to do when we have dry lips or skin.

Have you ever *thought* why petroleum jelly is called petroleum jelly? I didn't. For years. Then it hit me. It is a jelly made from *petroleum.* You know, the substance we make *petrol* from. The ingredient made from dead dinosaurs I mentioned above? That known carcinogen we have just been talking about? All smeared all over your lips and skin, waiting to go into your body.

Urgh no. I don't think so. There are amazing vegan, organic, 100% natural alternatives that work brilliantly. Or indeed learn to make your own!

My favourite vegan organic lip balms are made by Benecos and Living Nature.

Sunscreen – another Special Case

Synthetic sunscreen are toxic, and contain a cocktail of synthetic chemicals, which then sit on the skin and get heated up by the sun. According to the Melanoma Research Foundation, using synthetic sunscreen increases the risk of getting skin cancer.

Green People and Neal's Yard make natural sunscreens. There are also wonderful recipes online to make your own using coconut oil (which has a natural SPF), shea butter, zinc oxide and vitamin E oil.

Deodorants & Antiperspirants

Hopefully it isn't news to you that there are consistent findings of links between the use of these and breast cancer.

The good news is that there are some good natural deodorants on the market now (it has been hit or miss until the last few years). My favourite is the deodorant paste by Essential Blends.....I can do a 2 hour intensive dancing class and not smell a jot, which is amazing. You can also make your own using coconut oil (which has a natural SPF), shea butter, baking powder and arrowroot.

Face Painting & Glitter

Face glitter (made from plastic) is usually applied using glue. *Glue.* There is a much healthier option, as promoted by Eco Glitter Fun: using aloe vera gel. They are a great company by the way, I love them.

Perfumes

Perfumes contain many toxic ingredients. When you see the word "fragrance", what it really means is "hidden chemicals". Perfume manufactures and beauty products are allowed by law to keep its fragrance ingredients secret, as trade-secret formulas.

The Campaign for Safe Cosmetics commissioned laboratory tests that found 38 chemicals not listed on the labels in 17 branded fragrances (including Chanel, Giorgio Armani, Bath & Body Works, Old Spice, Calvin Klein, and others). The average was 14 unlisted chemicals, including hormone disrupters, chemicals that are known to cause allergic reactions, diethyphthalate (found in 97% of Americans, and linked to sperm damage), and chemicals that accumulate in fat tissue and are found in breast milk.

Perfumes can give people headaches, make people feel dizzy and nauseous. And here's the thing, they are designed to be emitted, so the chemicals evaporate and are inhaled by everyone the perfume-wearer meets. Fragrance is the new second-hand smoke.

We may choose to wear a synthetic perfume, and absorb and inhale the toxic ingredients, but we don't have the right to force others to do the same. We don't have the right to spread these chemicals to pregnant mothers and their unborn babies, to children, or to any other person or the environment.

This applies, by the way to laundry detergents, that are mentioned later – but the principle is the same – no one has the right to wear toxic chemicals that evaporate and cause harm to others.

And this applies to scented candles. Most are made with synthetic perfumes.

There are an increasing number of activists who are challenging others for using these toxic chemicals. One financial consultant in the US, for example, Karen Kraig instructs clients to show up for their appointments fragrance-free — and if someone goes into her office wearing perfume or with a strong shampoo or laundry soap smell, she asks them to leave. Her sensitivity to synthetic scents followed the 9/11 attacks and the dust that damage that followed. On other occasions has been known to make people wear a garbage bag over their clothes if the detergent smell was so fierce she couldn't endure it.".

She isn't alone – a growing number of activists, including those with multi-chemical sensitivities are asking friends, relatives, colleagues, employers, housemates, partners and clients to do the same.

Me included.

If you are affected, use your voice. Tell people. You won't be doing it just for you – you'll be doing it for people like you who are too embarrassed to say anything, for all the children and families and colleagues and the perfume wearers too. We can say it kindly, with understanding (most people don't realise the health risks), and respect. This isn't about being angry with people for doing what they have grown up or told is good for them, this is about sharing what you have learned and how the products affect you and others. Not everyone is ready to hear it first time, or even second, this involves talking about something that is counter to most people's beliefs, education and values. But sow a seed, let others know the impact and share your experience and learning as someone who is affected, and in time that seed will grow.

And what about alternatives? Neal's Yard Remedies make their own perfumes. Some more "natural" cheaper ones just contain a high alcohol content and they smell......well......cheap. Buy or make your own blend using 100% organic pure essential oils, diluted in a carrier oil.

Hand Sanitisers

Research is showing a noticeable rise in thyroid cancer in people who use hand sanitisers a lot – particularly healthcare professionals, and those who . One study of over 900 patients found that women with any occupational exposure at all were 48% more likely to develop thyroid cancer, and men were 300% more likely to develop thyroid cancer.

Following COVID, it became expected for people to use hand sanitisers. The thing is, they destroy the natural bacteria we all need to keep our immune systems healthy. I was working in a homeopathic pharmacy during COVID, were World Health Organisation (WHO) compliant sanitisers were available for all staff and customers. It stated very clearly on the label a warning that any contact with clothing or skin required immediate washing with water.

Hand sanitisers are not safe. Neal's Yard make a natural one using aromatherapy oils such as lavender which are naturally able to destroy pathogenic bacteria, whilst keeping healthy bacteria (and our immune system) alive. It's also possible to make your own simple one too if you feel using one is completely necessary.

Face Masks

Face masks, and all disposible medical equipment from cotton buds used in COVID testing kits are sprayed with ethylene oxide (EO). This is Class 1 carcinogen according to the International Agency for Research into Cancer (IARC).

Also face masks have holes bigger than a virus to pass through. Countless surgeons have pointed out that they are only used during surgery to prevent bits of spit and hair and skin from the surgical team entering the body of a patient. They can't and won't ever stop the transmission of a virus.

Toothpaste – another Special Case

The Federal Drug Administration (FDA) in the US labels fluoride a poison that should not be swallowed. It is a known neuro-toxin, and one study linked it to bone cancer in adolescents.

Use only fluoride-free toothpaste. And did you know that some white dental fillings contain fluoride, especially ones used for children? Insist on fluoride-free fillings at the dentist.

Fillings? Prevention is always better than cure – so cut out the sugar.

My favourite is the flouride free Kingfisher range, and I sometimes brush with pure organic turmeric powder, which is amazing as an anti-inflammatory for gums and antiseptic so wards off potential infections. Turmeric also (would you believe?!) whitens teeth! It's true I have seen the evidence for myself. It may stain everything else yellow, but slowly over time will make your teeth look amazing. Aloe Dent Whitening by the way isn't vegan, so I only use the sensitive one which is.

Washing up liquid – a *really* special case

This one is *really* important. When I was 17 years old, I had a massive realisation in a chemistry class. I asked my chemistry teacher why we didn't use washing up liquid when we washed up the glassware that we used for experiments. She told us that it takes 26 rinses to wash off the phosphates in the washing up liquid (off *glass*). In other words, the synthetic cleaning chemicals stick to the glass, and then react with whatever contents are added in any future experiments. This was back in 1992, and undoubtedly cleaning products have got stronger, so I wonder how many rinses it would take to remove the chemicals now.

Our bodies survive – and thrive – because of many chemistry reactions taking place at any one time – within them. The chemicals we literally eat off our plates and out of our mugs washed in conventional washing up liquid will affect the chemistry reactions in your body – and your health.

Those washing up liquid chemicals that we eat with the food on our plates, and with the teas in our mugs, go into our bodies, the bodies of the babies we carry, and in the water supply when we pee – so into the land too. The same happens with dishwasher powder – your dishwasher won't rinse the chemicals off completely, even though they do rinse.

You probably can't taste it. Your sense of smell and taste has been destroyed by them.

If you do a 6 week detox as I mentioned above, of all synthetic chemicals in your life, you will notice the difference. Get a really simple 100% natural washing up liquid, and notice how your sense of taste and smell return – and the chances are you will then taste washing up liquid on the crockery and cutlery you use when visiting friends who use conventional washing up liquids.

One of the biggest so called "natural" cleaning product range in the

UK, Ecover, available in all supermarkets, isn't by the way 100% natural. It's "plant based", with beautiful images of plants and leaves to make you think you are buying natural products. But you are not. So educate yourself, read ingredients, search online for what toxic problems there might be associated with the ingredients in your toiletries. In fact, since it was bought out by Unilever, the formulation has changed and is highly chemical.

Method, also owned by Unilever claims it's "non-toxic" - the toxicity standards it is referring to is set by the petrochemicals industry. So biased.

You will have to search around, as there aren't that many companies that make truly 100% natural products. Remember that even if it is 97% or 99% natural, that means there is SOME kind of synthetic chemical that might trigger an immune response in the body, and may damage the environment. In the appendix is a list of recommendations if you would like to access those.

My fave: Greenscents citrus washing up liquid (which is amazing, they are a brilliant company). They also have a lovely multi-surface cleaner and toilet cleaner too.

Air fresheners

As well as what I have shared in the section on perfumes, air fresheners contain chemicals hugely toxic to health, including phthalates, formaldehyde and petroleum derivatives.

Phthalates are hazardous chemicals known to cause cancer, hormonal abnormalities, birth defects, and reproductive problems.

So what can you do to make your home smell lovely?

- Use 100% pure organic aromatherapy oils in an oil burner or diffuser.
- In the kitchen, simmer slices of lemon in water, and the lemon will cleanse cooking smells from your kitchen.
- Frankincense (olibanum) oil is a great deodoriser and air (and energy) cleanser.
- Use white sage. Incense sticks can be made with artificial scents, white sage is a wonderful alternative.
- Use natural aromatherapy oil or essence sprays.

Anti-bacterial products

There are some products that harness the antibacterial properties found in nature. Lavender, for example, is a great example of a natural plant that has antibacterial properties. These don't destroy the gut bacteria, antibacterial plants seem to know the difference between destroying healthy gut bacteria and harmful bacteria, and they protect and keep safe our gut. Not so with synthetic antibacterial products such as triclosan, a common ingredient in handwashes, sanitisers, and other cleaning products, which destroys healthy bacteria, and therefore compromises our gut health, and therefore immunity.

Not to mention bleach, which is simply toxic to everyone and everything.

There are some wonderful completely natural alternatives that support gut health.

As well as being antibacterial, pure lavender oil is also anti-inflammatory and cooling, and is useful in a first aid kit for cuts to help prevent infection, and more cooling than water for minor burns. It can be applied neat (undiluted) to the skin.

So I use (or add) pure lavender oil products like Avalon hand soap.

Laundry Liquids & Powders

All of the major laundry washing products that are not 100% natural contain ingredients that are toxic to human health. This includes the "plant-based" and "non-toxic" ones like (at the time of writing) Ecover and Method. You are being fooled by clever marketing.

I would recommend you read the perfume section (above), as everything listed there is relevant here. In addition to that:

One piece of research by the Environmental Protection agency in the US in 2011 found more than 25 volatile organic compounds (VOCs), including seven hazardous air pollutants. The two carcinogens were acetaldehyde and benzene, which are considered to have no safe exposure level.

We breathe these chemicals in, they are washed into the water supply (and come back to us via our taps?), into our bodies either through the pores on our skin or because we breathe them in.

In addition to VOCs, some of the cleaning agents release formaldehyde (a known carcinogen), diethanolamine (skin and eye irritation and possible liver problems), nonlphenol ethoxylate (NPE – a neurotoxin, skin irritant and hormone disruptor) and petroleum distillates (linked to cancer and lung damage), contain bleach (lung, liver and kidney damage), phosphates and ethylene diamine tetraacetic acid (EDTA), which do not biodegrade and are toxic to the environment. In addition to this, optical brighteners are added to make clothes look brighter and they literally stick to the skin (and to everything they touch, including the drum of the washing machine, and don't like being washed off), and are linked with developmental and reproductive problems.

Fabric conditioners are not necessary – we have been made to believe that we need them to keep our clothes soft and smelling lovely. However what they do is coat your clothes with chemicals which is what makes them feel soft. These chemicals are inhaled because they release gases (VOCs).

Fabric softeners contain quaternary ammonium compounds, known to cause asthma and allergies, and some are known endocrine disruptors, and contribute to the formation of cancer-causing nitrosamines. They also contain phthalates (endocrine disruptors we talk about in other areas of this Chapter), diethanolamine (DEA) which interacts with other chemicals to form cancer-causing nitrosamines and 4-t-nonylphenol, another endocrine disrupting petrochemical.

Dryer sheets also contain toxic chemicals, one study found two carcinogens in one brand of scented sheets.

Need to hear anymore? Ditch the fabric softener. They were developed as a result of the introduction of clothes dryers that can excessively dry clothes, so you can just hang clothes to dry naturally instead, and your clothes will come out fine with just laundry wash.

And as I said in the perfume section, we may choose to wear a synthetic perfume, and absorb and inhale the toxic ingredients, but we don't have the right to force others to do the same. We don't have the right to spread these chemicals to pregnant mothers and their unborn babies, to children, or to any other person or the environment.

What can you do? Use soap nuts or 100% natural products. This is one area that I was always challenged by: I would find natural alternatives would leave my clothes smelling musty.

And then I happened to be experimenting, and found a wonderful combination that works really well:

A heaped tablespoon of BioD Nappy Cleanse plus 10ml of my favourite Greenscents Citrus Washing Up Liquid, or the unscented Washing Up Liquid with a few drops of Lavender Oil.

Nappy Cleanse uses a salt that deodorises and cleans clothes really well, the lavender handwash softens it and gives it a nice smell. Lavender is naturally antibacterial also. Soda crystals and bicarbonate of soda can be used too, soda crystals are great in a wash.

Clothing - non-organic cotton

Cotton, as it isn't used for food, is allowed to have more pesticides, insecticides and herbicides sprayed on them. According the Environmental Justice Foundation, even though cotton only occupies 2.4% of cropland globally, it burns through 16% of the insecticides used every year. According to the US Geological Survey, pesticide applications for cotton are 3 to 5 times greater per hectare than of pesticides tor corn. So in the US, at least 60% of farmers have switched to genetically modified cotton – which is leading to Roundup-resistant "superweeds", which require even more deadly herbicides.

You, your babies and your love ones wear clothes made with this every day. Then go to sleep in bedding made from it. The farmers that grow the crops are exposed to these horrendous chemicals. Not to mention what they do to the planet, and the children and adults in the sweatshops that often produce them.

The fact is that we simply don't have the right to poison each other and the planet, or to enslave the people who make our clothes. Just to look good. It ain't cool.

The good news is that more and more organic cotton options are becoming available, including in high street stores – and the more you buy, the more will become available. And people who buy hemp tend to be interested in Fairtrade, so many of these clothing companies make Fairtrade clothes too. Fairtrade is another subject altogether, and at times isn't always a guarantee of how well employees have been treated, so again do your research to find the best that you can. The more of us that do this, the more the price will come down to make these options accessible for everyone else.

Another solution is to start to demand from shops, and buy yourselves clothes made from………hemp.

Clothing - Hemp

Hemp is the planet's wonder plant. It can be used to make everything from paper to ropes, clothes, footwear, construction materials, natural plastics, natural sanitary products, and blankets. It lasts and lasts and lasts.

It can even be used to make tents, and amazingly, the hemp fibres naturally expand in rain making them waterproof, and so there is no need for tents to be sprayed with toxic waterproofing chemicals.

And the other amazing properties?

Hemp grows five times faster than cotton AND grows easily without the use of pesticides or herbicides. AND is naturally antibacterial and antiviral.

You know those clothes you buy with artificial antibacterial properties like socks? Those additional chemicals aren't needed in the first place, but even less so with hemp.

Again, the more you buy hemp products, the more that hemp will be used – here is another example where you can buy the change. I hope that soon fashion houses will pick up on this, and trend hemp clothing.

Again take note of what labels say and what they mean – there are some clothes that are made with hemp, but not *exclusively* and so can be made of a mixture of fibres. This is where reading about everything you buy makes you smarter than the marketing gurus.

Waterproof Clothing, Tents, Sleeping Bags & Walking Boots

Greenpeace conducted a study that found that hazardous chemicals were found "widely present" in a range of outdoor gear, and found toxic chemicals in products by brands including Jack Wolfskin, North

Face, Patagonia, Mammut, Norrona and Salewa. They particularly found per- and polyfluorinated chemicals (PFCs). They literally shed into the environment and don't break down easily, so persist. Studies have shown PFCs can have negatively affect the immune system, the reproductive system and are potentially carcinogenic. They have been found in human blood and in the livers of Arctic polar bears.

Again you have a choice! Some of the more traditional types of clothing made of natural fibres by tribespeople who live in cold climates, such as the Himalayas are waterproof, breathable, windproof and warm. The delight of students, hippies and regulars at Glastonbury festival, these kind of clothes might not (yet) be designed to look like something you can wear to a business meeting, or to a glitzy night out, but there is a gap in the market that will hopefully be filled by a cool designer and entrepreneur. Hint hint to designers and entrepreneurs wanting a new direction.

Hemp is again an amazing product, as mentioned above – waterproof and windproof, and more and more designers are making cool clothes with hemp, often sold on places like Etsy.

Tents made from hemp or canvas last longer and are so much better for health – especially if not sprayed with waterproofing and other chemicals, which companies don't use.

School Uniforms

In the UK, every school uniform comes coated in Teflon or other stain repellant / non-stick coating, that is a carcinogen. Teflon is said to be carcinogenic only at high temperatures but it doesn't break down in the environment, and when children get hot and sweaty, there aren't any guarantees that some of the coating isn't entering the body. Also, the US has decided to restrict the use of a chemical used in the manufacture of Teflon......any alarm bells ringing yet?

This is a classic example of where many of us aren't erring on the side of caution.......but these are our precious children.

In the UK, the only way to buy uniform that is NOT coated in Teflon or any other stain repellant or non-stick coating is to buy organic uniform, which isn't in everyone's price range. It means you have to iron the uniforms, but at least the uniform is a healthy one.

For the time my son had to wear uniform, I refused to buy him the standard issue uniform with the school logo badge on the sweater, and told the school why. The staff there *loved* me as was clear from the rolling of their eyes. But we have to do this as parents. Make a stand. You are a powerful voice and consumer. Demand your child's school provides other options that are not coated in synthetic (and in this toxic) chemicals, and talk to other parents about this issue and get them on board.

In the UK, Eco Outfitters is a great company for organic school uniforms.

Lifestyle - Your Kitchen & Home

Stainless Steel Cookware

Aluminium pans have been known to be a health risk for decades – aluminium is said to be a major contributing factor for Alzheimers'. When I did a school project on saucepans at the age of 16, I knew nothing about them, and was amazed that people were still using them then.

Move forward a couple of decades and still the message isn't clear. Ditch aluminium pans and non-stick pans. The non-stick coating is said to be carcinogenic only at high temperatures (when a pan overheats). But non-stick coating does come off the pans, especially when a metal object is used with them. It doesn't break down in the environment. And as mentioned in the section on school uniforms, the US has decided to restrict the use of a chemical used in the manufacture of Teflon...... and as I also said there: any alarm bells ringing yet?

This is a classic example of where many of us aren't erring on the side of caution.......and erring on the side of cautions now remains what it was for me at 16, which is ditch anything that isn't stainless steel.

This applies to plastic utensils too. Stainless steel is the best and safest choice in the kitchen. If you must have non-stick, then a enamel-coated iron pan, such as those made by Le Creuset are a good alternative. Le Creuset also make standard non-stick pans, so do check that you are definitely buying an enamel-coated iron pan produced by whichever company you buy from. The enamel coating is similar to a glass coating, and does not contain the toxic chemicals found in standard non-stick cookware.

Clingfilm, plastic and putting food in plastic bags

Any food with any fat content will absorb hormone disrupting estrogenic properties in plastic. Use ceramic bowls, glass or steel containers, or do as our grandparents did - put the lid on the pan, and put it in the fridge, or put a plate over a bowl.

Children's plastic plates and cups

We lived for hundreds (thousands?!) of years without them. Using ceramic plates not only prevents exposure to chemicals in plastic, especially from warmed food, which we surely don't want our children to be exposed to, but also stops the production of these oil based products (which uses petroleum and the drive for oil creates wars). Want to stop wars and save the environment? Give your children ceramic or steel plates. Yes, they might break them, but they will also learn the importance of being careful with their plates and cups, carrying their food with care and attention, being mindful and present in the moment.

Microwaves

When studies compare the same meal, one microwaved and the other not, insects will never touch the one that has been microwaved. Microwaves destroy the digestive enzymes in food, and literally create dead food. I would suggest that Nature's Medicine Code and the Golden Spiral within are destroyed using this cooking process.

Mattresses, TVs, electrical goods, furniture, carpets & furnishings

Most mattresses and sofas, car seats, curtains and upholstered furniture proudly display that they meet legal safety standards to be flame retardant. However are you aware of the toxic mix of chemicals that they are sprayed with? Arguably, these are the most toxic substances you can bring into your home. Brominated flame retardants have been linked to a range of health problems and diseases including infertility, birth defects, behavioural problems in children, and liver, kidney, testicular and breast cancers and autoimmune disorders. Because they are fat soluble, they accumulate in the fat in the body, including in breast tissue, and are found in breast milk.

Formaldehyde, a known carcinogen used to preserve dead bodies, is found in most flat-pack furniture, often in the adhesives used in composite wood products such as particle board, fiberboard and plywood.

Buy a mattress second hand so that it will been "off-gassed" as much as possible – had some of the toxic chemicals released before the mattress gets to you.

Or even better, buy a 100% natural chemical free mattress.

This is one area where veganism can be a challenge – the only legal exemption for the use of flame retardants is when wool is used instead, because wool is naturally flame retardant.

Two wonderful UK companies making 100% natural mattresses are Natural Mat and the more affordable but still excellent SnoozelGreen.

Also if you can, it helps to buy pure wood furniture.

I have a friend who has no known allergies, yet can't hold carpet samples, because her fingers go numb and tingly from exposure to the chemicals in them. Wool carpets or natural carpets are available, but also ask that carpet fitters nail the carpets down, rather than glue them (it won't surprise you to know that the glues are toxic).

You can also have your own curtains handmade if you can afford it (or make them yourselves!) so that they won't be sprayed with flame retardant, stain repellant and crease-free chemicals.

TVs and other electrical goods (mobile phones, laptops) are another source of flame retardant chemicals, "just in case" the electrical item blows up. Speak to people, friends, family, relatives, and the producers and sellers themselves – most don't realise there is an issue, and when more and more do, it will be easier to bring a change to the use of these toxins in our environment.

Apple, Dell don't use brominated flame retardants or PVC in its products, they aren't added to HP Notebooks anymore and other companies are committing to make the same changes.

Working life

Stop working so damn hard. It stops you connecting to yourself, or spending time with loved ones. Disconnection weakens the immune system. Connection; relationships, love, doing things that make our heart and soul sing – all those connections strengthen the immune system. There is a lot to be said for the inspiring policy changes coming from some Scandanavian countries that are now moving to 6 hour working days, with no change in levels of income. We need balance – harmonia – in all areas of our lives in order to be well. You won't, on your deathbed, think "at least I stayed that extra 3 hours at work every day!". You will wish you had spent more time with the people who you love and who love you.

Condoms

Did you know that the white powdery substance on condoms is actually milk powder? You know....that pus, hormone, antibiotic, GMO and growth hormone filled substance we talked about in the diet section?

Spermicides? Those synthetic chemicals that are agents of death? Ladies - do you want that in your fru-fru? I didn't think so. Spermicide-free vegan condoms are the way to go.

Vegan condoms such as those made by Glyde are a healthier alternative.

Sex toys

Did you know that most sex toys contain phthalates? Those hazardous chemicals we talked about used in air fresheners known to cause cancer, hormonal abnormalities, birth defects, and reproductive problems?

Ladies - want that in your fru fru too? No, I didn't think so.

Well, the good news is that some companies make phthalate-free sex toys, some companies even make them using crystals. Your vagina and/or your partner's vagina are worth it. One company, Gaia, makes vibrators made from plant plastics. Now, they aren't organic (I hope that is the next step), but that is – for what we are used to – impressive. Am I allowed to also suggest some organic vegetables might be the healthiest option of all? Well I just did.

Lubricants

Organic natural lubricants all the way........conventional lubricants can contain petroleum jelly, petroleum-based ingredients, parabens, phenoxyethanol (high concentrations have been associated with reproductive damage, lowered immunity and lower nervous system function in newborns, propylene glycol (used in antifreeze) and others. Even glycerin, which can seem safe, is a form of sugar, and so can increase the risk of candida (thrush).

Or use 100% pure organic aloe vera gel, coconut oil (although not to be used with a condom). Yes organic water-based lube is a good alternative, although contains gums like xanthan gum which we mentioned in the section on diet.

Sanitary products

1,4-dioxane, a byproduct of the production of polysorbate-20, a preservative used in some baby wipes and cosmetics (including ones labeled "pure"). The Organic Consumers Organization in the US has produced a well referenced factsheet that describes how the levels of 1,4-dioxane in many personal care products are 1000 times higher than the levels that cause cancer in laboratory animals.

In addition to that, sanitary are often made with cotton. Cotton that is not organic is allowed to use many more pesticides than those allowed on food. Want that in your fru fru?

As well a lot of bleach, which is what makes the products white.

The cramping pain you have when you have your period? It may be caused by the dioxins in the sanitary products that cause you to produce more blood than you otherwise would.

So what can you do?

Choose only 100% organic natural sanitary products. There are some amazing beautifully designed 100% organic cloth sanitary pads that are washable that are also being made, that, when soaked in 100% natural nappy cleanse, wash out amazingly and are super comfy.

Just one final thought while we are here. I spent 8 years taking the contraceptive pill, and years using tampons. And then someone explained something to me that just *made sense*. Periods and the menstrual cycle are about flow. If you artificially stop the flow, or block the flow (with tampons), you are interfering with your flow – with the flow of energy, and life, and your dreams and desires, and health throughout all of you. I haven't used tampons since, and feel much better for it.

This, like with everything else, is about to learning to listen to your body and what helps your body feel good (and in this case, like a true and real woman). This is one of the functions of your period.

Toilet Paper

Most toilet papers are made with the use of bleach, especially the bright white ones. Want that wiped on your fru-fru ladies? I didn't think so.

The good news is that some companies make unbleached toilet paper and also using organic materials.

Gardening

Pesticides, weedkillers, herbicides, insecticides......we know they cause cancer and a multitude of other health problems. There are a plethora of suggestions online and through gardening experts about how to grow a healthy garden without using these toxic chemicals that are a poison to you and your family. Do some research, experiment and have fun.

Think it's hard and can't be done? My Mum grew a remarkable garden of paradise at her London home, with a menagerie of fruit trees, apples, plums, nectarines, pears, as well a beautiful vegetable patch, and many species of roses – all done without the use of synthetic chemicals that cause death, completely naturally with a love of life and nature and what nature can achieve when supported to thrive.

Planet Natural is a great resource online for organic gardening tips. Organic seeds can be bought from a range of sites online, including grasses, trees, herbs and vegetables.

I made a homeopathic remedy of the Golden Spiral, and add this to my plants, and they thrive because of it. You can watch a video of the experiment I did when I tested it on sugar snaps pea seeds, and the remarkable results on my website!

Paints

Paints and finishes release low level toxic emissions into the air for years after they have been applied in the form of VOCs. Professional painters report higher incidences of liver, kidney and nervous system damage, and traditional paints should be avoided by those with asthma and breathing difficulties.

The good news is that there are many companies that now produce completely natural paint. It may be expensive, but the finish of the one I have used (Ecos Paints) is amazing.

Cars

This is a funny one to include in a book about the health of your body, isn't it? So why is it here?? Many cities around the world are choked with pollution – with disease code petrochemicals that cause asthma, allergies, rhinitis, and lead to death. So what can you do? If you are fortunate enough to be able to afford an electric car, I would suggest that you doing so will contribute to fewer toxic pollutants in the air that make people sick (and lead to people dying). AND the more people that buy electric cars, the cheaper they will become for those on lower incomes too – the price will fall. If you also charge them ONLY using electricity that has come from a company using 100% green life-giving energy (not nuclear), then you really be making a difference to the health and well-being of the planet. (And no longer buying oil, which we know is the reason for many wars we see in the world, so you would be helping to bring peace too!).

But there is a bit of a issue even with electric cars – usually they are seen as a luxury, and furnished with leather (unnecessary in an ethical, compassionate, cruelty free world), sprayed with flame retardant chemicals and the off-gassing of the plastics used as well, means that it can take 3 years to off-gas a new car from all of the toxic chemicals found within them.

Most people who are currently buying electric cars are doing so because they care about the environment, so having the care applied to the manufacture and production processes feels really important for companies to understand. Again use your voice here, write to companies and tell them how you want to spend money with them, but that they need to go further in what they have to offer, and to make more ethical choices in production.

To me, this isn't a choice, or an option. I think this is actually a moral duty for the health of each other and the planet, for those that can afford to do so. People are literally dying when we use our cars fuelled with petrol. Through the air they breathe and from the wars petrol fosters. Go on. You can do it. Be The Change. Buy The Change.

Phi Architecture

Did you know that some architects design buildings and homes taking Phi mathematics into consideration, with a view to building healthy homes that facilitate a great flow of energy. It may not be something you or your family can look into at this point in your lives, but when re-decorating your home or purchasing a new one, just being aware of this may give you some choices to help build a home based on the mathematics of nature.

Sports - Golf & Boules

Golf courses are sprayed with a toxic cocktail of weedkillers (herbicides), insecticides, fungicides and other chemicals. We know that these can cause cancers in humans, as well as other health problems and damage the local wildlife and pollute the rivers – eventually entering the water table – sometimes our drinking water.

This one is a real "Be The Change". Even though you may be asked to do business and network through golfing, be willing to suggest alternatives – and explain why. Re-think whether it is really necessary to choose to play a sport that causes so much human and environmental damage, when there are many many other sports to choose from with less toxicity to you, your loved ones and the animals and ecosystem. You will carry those chemicals home on your clothes, walk them into your home through your shoes, do you really want your children and families to deal with that?

If you feel you simply cannot make that choice, speak to your golf course about changing its golf course management to move to only natural means of managing it, and inspire other players you know to do the same.

Banking, Insurance & Investments

I can imagine you are wondering how the world of financial services has *anything* to do with all of this.

Your bank, unless it is a completely ethical bank, is investing in, and supporting companies that have been destroying your health, *your* environment and the air you breathe and the water you drink, the companies that produce substances we know cause disease, and pharmaceutical companies that we know cause ill health.

The provider of our home insurance may also be insuring a pharmaceutical company or oil company.

And we may be investing in companies that directly or indirectly support making money from pharmaceutical companies, the oil industry and the killing of innocent people through war.

We literally create the circumstances happening in the world with the money we spend.

So if you can, move your money. All of it. Now. Every last penny.

Stop investing in companies that are not 100% ethical. Many companies are good at promoting some of the "good" things they may be doing for people or the environment, but when you look past the glossy outer Corporate Social Responsibility marketing, it's only covering up shoddy practices elsewhere.

Investing is seen as a game. It isn't a game for the people affected negatively by the companies helping you get rich. People affected by disease, war, poverty. So take your money elsewhere, and allow it to make you feel good just by where it is and what it is doing in the world. Our world and the people on it are too precious to be used in any way that doesn't bring health and happiness to all.

Do you think sometimes that you, as one person, can't make the change? I think we all feel like that sometimes. When you have times of doubt, remember what has happened with veganism. It has *exploded exponentially.* Restaurant chains now even have *separate vegan menus!* That is because of the vegans who one by one made the change. And now it's entered the collective consciousness.

More and more people are changing the world by how they spend their money, the explosion in organic food and more natural products is another testament to that.

So what we do with our money – with every single penny of it – can make our world *amazing.*

As we talked about in Part 5: Emotional Health & Happiness, life is to be *experienced.* Positive psychologists are consistently finding that once all our needs are met financially, any more income doesn't make us happier. Not the extra TVs, or the extra few cars, or the extra big house. Our mind might *think* it wants those things, but those feelings of happiness are fleeting, it's the feelings of making a difference to others, of connecting that last. I What *does* make us happier is making a difference to others, and in the world, as the Action For Happiness list of 10 Keys to Happier Living tells us.

So if we are financially abundant, and have what we need, doing amazing things instead like buying up the rainforest so that it cannot be used for logging or destroying the habitats of orangutans would be brilliant. Supporting genius companies cleaning up our oceans of plastic. Protecting sea-life, because they need our help. Investing in start-ups doing genius healthy things with food and the environment and natural health. Getting involved with organisations that support humanity and bring a wonderful life to those whose lives haven't been wonderful.

The *harmony* in our mental health that will come from living from a place of true happiness will support our physical health too.

Using our money as a force for *good* in this world, and *only* good. We will feel *amazing* and the planet and humanity and animals and people will benefit from this exponentially.

I don't care what any country believes about its borders, we are one world, and one family, and we have to look after each other. How we use our money – and our relationship and beliefs about money – define that.

Geoengineering & artificial weather patterns

When I first wrote Nature's Medicine Code, we already had geoengineering - the process of modifying (engineering) weather patterns - which started in the 1950s. Since the publication of the first edition, we have seen a huge increase in artificial weather patterns that include Solar Radiation Management (SRM), which is described on NASA's website - the spray of white across our skies to block out the sun (supposedly to "protect us" from the sun's rays, through to cloud seeding, artificial winds & storms.

How do we know? During the first lockdown, everywhere around the world had natural weather patterns again, because planes weren't allowed to fly in the skies. We got to experience our weather - as it is supposed to be. We need the sun. The sun gives us life, energy, happiness and joy. We feel more vibrant, alive, energised, activated.

Artificial winds and storms generated using weather stations such as

HAARP in Alaska (but there are others around the world) use an artificially generated spiral, which then throws out the natural golden spiral weather patterns of naturally occurring winds around the world.

Our energy fields flow with the natural spirals in the world around us - so artificially generated weather patterns will also throw out the spirals in our own bodies and energy fields. We see more vertigo, dizziness, low mood, exhaustion.

The white chemtrail sprays contain a range of chemicals including lanthanides metals, strontium, rubidium, barium, arsenic, lithium, cadmium and others.

This book has a hopeful message - and this includes this one.

Firstly, the more of us know about this, the more that we can ensure that change happens. All we have to do is look to the skies, and for those of us that are 45 years and older, to remember the weather and blue skies of our childhoods. When enough of us know, we can bring about change.

Secondly, one of the most powerful things we can do is to work with the Golden Spiral, to keep us in alignment with our own. This can be done either by taking the homeopathic remedy of the Golden Spiral, or an essence, both of which I made in 2020, the only true original source of either of these. Others have since made their own, but the ones I have are the only true (and most energetically vital) originals, following 15 years of working with this incredible geometry as outlined in this book.

The only true original source of Golden Spiral as an essence is from the

Blueprint Essences® range of essences that I created. Nothing else is a true original. What I have prepared is the only truly genuine original source of Golden Spiral in the world. It has the greatest vibration. Taking this essence supports our alignment with our naturally occurring Golden Spiral - the natural spiral of our body, mind, soul & life, irrespective of what goes on around it.

There is also a Flower of Life essence in the Blueprint Essences® range, as well as other geometric symbols that connect us with Phi mathematics and the vibration of life and love and reawaken us to our power - all of which are the only true originals of these in the world. I have also made all of these as homeopathic remedies separately too.

Homeopathy can help support our ability to clear and detoxify from the toxins we are exposed to in our world, including from what is sprayed from the skies. Practical homeopaths are trained in how to do this.

These can be added to soils and plants to support healthy plant growth. There is a video of an experiment I did with using Golden Spiral on plants, compared with not using it, on my website, showing how amazingly plants respond to being grown in water with the Golden Spiral in them; not only are stems stronger but root growth is amazing - and we need strong healthy roots to absorb nutrients from the soil.

Finally, when there are artificial winds, it helps to wear silicone ear plugs, especially when sleeping. It is common for people to experience headaches, dizziness, vertigo, confusion, disorientation and exhaustion with artificially generated winds, because we literally are thrown off balance - and our balance is strongly linked to our ears. So having ear plugs in place brings containment and steadiness to our body and energy field.

We are the change we have been waiting for. These practices will come to an end when enough of us are aware of them, and champion a return to natural weather patterns, natural blue skies and sunshine.

Mental Health & Emotional Wellbeing

In addition to all that has been suggested in the sections on Healthcare and Diet, I would also suggest these steps:

1) Happiness

Positive psychology is a branch of psychology that is interested in identifying what helps us to live happier, more fulfilled lives – lives where we don't just survive but where we *thrive and flourish.*

One of the interesting and consistent research findings coming out of the field of positive psychology focuses on our relationship with and perspective on achievement, success and money. It turns out that once all our needs are met financially, any more income doesn't make us happier. Not the extra TVs, or the extra few cars, or the extra big house. Our mind might *think* it wants those things, but those feelings of happiness are fleeting, it's the feeling of making a difference to others, of having wonderful experiences, of feeling connected to the people we love – those are the things that *really* matter.

Some of this research is discussed in a film available online called *Happy The Movie* by Roko Belić. The Director travelled the world to identify what makes people happy, and draws upon research from positive psychology. It's a really wonderful way to spend a couple of hours.

A lack of happiness – anything that brings disharmony to what we think and how we feel – brings disharmony to the body. Our orchestra struggles to play a beautiful symphony when we are sad, as well as when we have a physical illness or are struggling with too many toxins. But ensuring your happiness is probably the best way to strengthen your conductor – a happy conductor will be easily able to inspire the whole orchestra to play that beautiful symphony. An unhappy one will feel overwhelmed and find it hard to inspire and lead, an angry one will just shout at the musicians who will stop playing beautiful rhythmic harmonious sounds.....but a *happy* conductor, who feels fulfilled and joyous can do *anything.* Our immune system is like that. When happy, it can do *anything.* It *thrives.*

Action for Happiness is an organisation that brings together the latest research in positive psychology. It's patron is the Dalai Lama, and it talks about 10 Keys to Happier Living. They are:

1) Do things for others
2) Connect with people
3) Take care of your body
4) Live life mindfully
5) Keep learning new things
6) Have goals to look forward to
7) Find ways to bounce back
8) Look for what's good
9) Be comfortable with who you are
10) Be part of something bigger.

A person living in these ways, living on what truly nourishes them based on the mathematics, geometry and sound vibrations of life, love and health has a happy and balanced mind, body and soul. A happy, thriving orchestra playing a beautiful wonderful harmonious *symphony.*

2) Education

If Nature's Medicine Code is found throughout the body then it must be found in the mind. The mind has two halves; two hemispheres that were first described by Roger Sperry in 1961.

The left hemisphere (half) of the brain is concerned with all things logical (think Left: Logical) and the right hemisphere is concerned with all things creative (think Right: cReative).

So the left deals with numbers, and lists, and logic, facts, mathematics, structure. The right with the senses – sound, music, sight, patterns, the "big picture".

What does this mean? For us to learn effectively, the *whole* brain has to be involved. This will involve the *whole* of the Golden Spiral and the Phi mathematics and that is found in our bodies – and so must exist in the brain.

We can't have the tenors only singing in the orchestral choir to sing in the whole orchestral symphony, we have to have the sopranos too.

In large parts of the western world, our education system is focused on – and values – learning that stimulates one part of the brain, the left-hemisphere (logic and facts)...... to the exclusion of the right. This, in addition to the pressure of exams that don't suit more creatively-minded children, means that children experience learning that isn't whole-brain learning. This is disharmonious to healthy overall development, and happiness – and this in turn leads to poor mental health and life outcomes.

Concerns have been raised by educational psychologists across the board, and one of the most watched (and wonderful) TED Talks is the one by Sir Ken Robinson titled: "Do schools kill creativity?". It has had over 50 million views.

Countries like Norway, Iceland, Denmark, Sweden and Holland are leading the way in changing the way children spend their valuable time at school. But we can all help by looking into education and researching all of the possibilities and evidence into more holistic and healthy approaches to education. More alternative approaches like Steiner Education and Montessori provide whole child approaches to learning and health, and many Silicon Valley execs are educating their children in these ways. Talk about what you learn about with your child's school and parents, and encourage change through your discussions and actions.

3) Social Media & Gaming

As we have already discussed, anything that brings disharmony to the mind will bring disharmony to the body, in fact naturopaths and holistic medicine practitioners are usually interested in what has happened to someone *emotionally* that has led to a physical disease.

Research by psychologists into the negative effects of social media on young people, with rising levels of anxiety and depression, is now well established. The problem only seems to be growing.

That in addition to some children and adults playing death, killing and shooting games, sometimes for hours at a time – the discomfort that will cause the subconscious mind will play out in mental health problems, relationship problems, physical ill health.

When we take part in disharmonious activities, the effect is disharmonious mental, emotional and physical health.

We can change that. As parents, we have a choice. There is a reason that parents of Silicon Valley executives don't give their kids access to this technology. If the technical creators don't give these to their kids, then that should mean something for ours.

It's not all bad; YouTube was found in research to generally have a positive impact – which makes sense, as there is so much wonderful, positive, life and happiness and health enhancing content on YouTube.

But letting our children be children really supports their physical, mental and emotional health. Children need to climb trees, get dirty, play sports, build Lego (which is soon to be made using sustainable plastics by the way), draw, paint, play with other children using their imaginations. When we let them get bored, once their wingeing and whining stops, they will come up with things to do and create using their imaginations, and learn self-confidence, independence (not addiction), resilience and freedom along the way. It took 2 weeks for my then 4-year old to remember how to creatively play once I got rid of our telly (and those were a painful 2 weeks I will always remember). But then I woke up one morning to find him building and making things all by himself, and he has continued ever since. We still watch films sometimes, and they are a treat because of it that we enjoy with homemade organic popcorn, but I was amazed to see how little creative thinking he could do when we had a TV and he wasn't even watching more than 1 hour a day.

The same applies to travelling by car or train. If children can't learn to be bored during a car journey or a train journey, they won't learn to stare out of the window and see the world go by, to lose track of time, to fight (and make-up) with their siblings. Planes are different, as the journeys can be longer, and we are in a really confined space with others, and part of the experience is the films that we can watch, but cars and most train journeys can be managed without technological influence. If children need an iPad as soon as they start travelling, they are learning never to have an inner stillness, and they learn instant gratification which is problematic as adults. They will never learn to be comfortable with discomfort – and so will always reach for and depend upon external sources to soothe or avoid feeling anything uncomfortable. We need to feel discomfort to grow emotionally, and need to be able to do so without numbing ourselves. When we let children be bored – or sing songs, or play i-spy or read a book or listen to an audiobook, we are helping them emotionally and mentally. We think *we* are the ones who won't cope if they get demanding, but they will be OK and so will you. Other adults might even step in to help you by distracting your kids if they become challenging – this is wonderful because it takes a village to raise a child, and we can all help each other in this way.

Our children's health – being harmonious and balanced – requires us to be willing to say no to those things we know causes harm, that brings *disharmony* - explaining why, letting them have fun, but being the strong ones to safeguard their mental and physical health.

And like with sugar, I was a Mum that took my son when he was younger to friend's houses, and let them know we didn't do much gaming, and finished with a "Is that OK with you?" No-one ever says "no that's not OK" – because we all *know* that's the best approach for our kids, we all feel guilty when they've had too much screen time. We *know* this stuff. Our children need us to protect them as much as we can.

So be strong. Have courage. It's not easy, I really know – and it takes a lot of gulping and breathing before speaking sometimes. But the more of us that do it now, the easier it will be for other parents to do the same. And in the process we are showing our kids the way to strength, resilience, balance and courage too.

4) Mindset

We naturally have what psychologists call a *negative bias*. This is a phenomenon where we give more psychological weight to bad experiences, thoughts, emotions and social interactions than to good ones.

Well that fits with the orchestra analogy perfectly – it has traditionally been the case with using *any skill* - the conductor and players will notice more what went *wrong* so it can be practiced and corrected before a performance requiring perfection. The same has been true of education, of work skills, raising children, of almost anything any of us have learned.

Thanks to developments in positive psychology, and neuroscience, we now know that the way to get the most out of others – the best way to engage them – is to focus on the positives, to be encouraging, and to focus on *strengths.*

Strengths is a branch of positive psychology that focuses on helping individuals, businesses and communities to harness their strengths.

But what are strengths?

Strengths are what give you energy when you use them, and so make you feel good. They are linked to your values and to who you are, and "playing to your strengths" is a way of harnessing what gives you energy to your work and life so you are more successful, thrive, happier.

Knowing my strengths and what gives me energy – and what I find draining – helped me a lot. I got to see my areas of "non-strength" – what drains me. My negative bias and negative self-talk would give me such a hard time about the things I struggled to do, and when I realized it is just because they aren't my strengths, I was able to be more at peace with myself. I used to *really* beat myself up. Imagine what that did to my immune system! Knowing this means I have been able to put strategies in place, and it's become an opportunity to connect with others who have strengths in areas that I don't.

When we know more about ourselves, and realize its *normal* and indeed *desireable* to be "imperfect" – that what we lack is actually an opportunity to connect with others who have what we need, we find ourselves coming into balance. It helps us feel at peace with ourselves, and who we are, accepting who we are, and what we like and don't like and what energises us and what doesn't.

It makes it easier to be aware of limiting beliefs about ourselves and the world and to let them go.

It also helps to understand your strengths, because one other challenge they can highlight for us is what happens when we *overuse* them. Sometimes, when we feel anxious or lack confidence, we fall back on our strengths to help us, but we can go our balance in how we apply them. For example, one of my strengths is enthusiasm. When I feel anxious sometimes, I can go into overdrive – or overplay – that strength, become overly enthusiastic as a way of trying to hide my nervousness. But other people can feel and sense and see and hear when we overuse our strengths, and step back, because it's too much for them to deal with. For me, it's enthusiasm, but some people whose strengths are in critical thinking (great analytical thinking) can become overly critical when in overdrive. Others with a compassion strength can give so much of their time to help others that their overdrive leaves them with a lack of energy to look after themselves, and their health can suffer. So what gives us energy can sabotage us too, if we don't use our strengths in balance. Having an awareness of strengths – and which of our strengths can go into overdrive gives us an awareness that helps us to stay in balance in how we use them.

And knowing our strengths – and areas of non-strength (what doesn't give us energy) is what stops the negative bias in it's tracks. By focusing on strengths, on the positives, we find solutions to problems more easily, and feel more confident and are more likely to choose activities and careers that we love, and are more like to succeed in. This is choosing a positive mindset – a mindset of possibilities. And this can *only* be good for our mental, emotional, physical and spiritual health and wellbeing. This helps us remain in *harmony.*

And the musicians in the orchestra? Each will have their own strengths. When they play to their individual strengths, the passion within which they play will be invigorating and the symphony created will be exceptionally beautiful.

How can you find out about your strengths? Strengthscope® is my favourite tool for assessing strengths – I am biased, I worked for the company, but I think it's fab and it's the only one endorsed by the British Psychological Society. It's not free, but its' easy to use and understand and is the only tool I know where you can see how your strengths work together to help or hinder you. If you would like to use a free version, Martin Seligman's Values in Action (VIA) tool is wonderful and has an added spiritual dimension.

This is a theory and a book about health, but our health doesn't just depend on our individual circumstances. If all of our organs are singing a harmonious symphony, we have a healthy body. But we are all connected and part of the same wider orchestra. If the people, plants, animals and environment are singing a harmonious symphony, we have a healthy world. A truly healthy happy body needs a healthy happy world. It is in *your power* to make all the changes in your life that you need to make that help you build true and lasting health inside and out.

Epilogue

It is only in the writing of this book that I came to understand a mantra my mother used to live by. She would work away in the paradise of a garden that she had grown, tending to her beloved tomatoes and the other vegetables she grown along with all of her adored roses and fruit trees, and say – again, and again – a mantra.

Looking back at all I have written, I realise the profound wisdom in it – wisdom I simply, as you will understand when I say it, I didn't really understand in my teenage city girl view of life and the world.

To give you some context, I would like to describe my mother - Branka's - village, Rača (pronounced Racha) near Kragujevac (pronounced Kraguyevatz) in Serbia. For anyone who has watched Sasha Baron-Cohen's film *Borat,* my mother's village was just like his, my mother's best friend's house was identical to his in the film. My mother lived in a house without running water, when we visited my grandmother as children, we would get our water from the well in the farm across the road. We would bathe in winter in the tin bath that lived under the single metal bed in my grandmother's kitchen, with water heated on the wood stove using the wood my grandmother had spent all summer chopping with an axe. I spent the winter when I was 12 years old, sitting on that bed, in the warmth of the kitchen, listening to Duran Duran on my Sony Walkman, and reading *The Lord of the Rings.* In the summer, we would do the washing up in bowls under the sweetly scented linden flower tree outside my grandmother's front door. When we phoned to speak to my grandmother, we would phone the farm, as my grandmother didn't have a telephone, and I would hear the farmer's wife running, shouting across the road "Dano! DANO! Branka na telephonu!!!" ("Dana! DANA! Branka's on the telephone!") This was considered backwards, a life of poverty, but even though I was a "Dama iz Londona" as a famous Yugoslavian song said ' "A Dame from London", in the villagers eyes simply because of where I lived, I could still see how rich my grandmother and my mother were for the simplicity of this life.

My grandmother was an illiterate farm hand, my mother very intelligent, but had had a difficult life and a hard time at school, in her tiny village, in the former Yugoslavia, as it was then, so she left school at 15 with no qualifications. She started life in London as a domestic in a hotel in Paddington, and eventually became a seamstress. She adjusted well, considering, to London life when she emigrated. She loved its diversity and meeting people from around the world, especially immigrants from the West Indies speaking in Patwa which she thought was brilliant. She was in total awe of the tube map, and I remember her once explaining to me, whilst we were waiting on a station platform for a train, why it was so special and magical to her. Selfridges was her favourite place to take us on Saturdays. But her garden was her favourite place of all, and her stunning happy abundant garden amazingly completely died immediately after she did. It was like without her tremendous tender love and care, it didn't want to exist either.

And as she pottered around within it, there was one thing she would say over and over, based on a gut feeling that couldn't be suppressed or denied; a gut feeling, and a knowing, about the world we live in.

My mother may not have been educated, but she was wise.

""Niko nemože da mi kaže da je dzravo staviti hemikalije na hranu ili na telo. Niko." Translated it means:

"No-one can tell me that it is healthy to put [synthetic] chemicals on
our food or on our bodies. No-one."

-   Branka Matić

And that, I think – is the crux of this book. I have taken you on a journey through mathematics, science, music, medicine, the body, and life. But ultimately the message is a simple one. It's a message my mother shared with me many years ago.

So I would like to finish by dedicating this book to my dear Mama Branka, the inspiration for all you have read here.

Some final thank yous.......

As well as my dear Mama and my boy who I dedicate this to, this book simply would not have happened without the amazing ideas-sharing, discussions, encouragement, love and support of some great great friends.

So I would particularly like to thank:

Zoe Scanlan, a homeopathic practitioner and teacher of homeopathy who saw early drafts and whose passion and enthusiasm for what I am doing, and how I have presented the ideas in this book carried me for weeks and weeks.

Liz Angell, a homeopath and one of my tutors at The Southern College of Homeopathy, who was the first to see the first draft of the book, and whose wonderful encouragement helped motivate me to finish what I had begun.

Micheline Edwards, a brilliant Health Coach who runs wonderful courses from her family farm connecting people back to real food and real health, who gave me so much encouragement, and read the early drafts, giving me brilliant suggestions for its expansion and growth.

The neverending love, support and friendship of my dear friends Vickie Simner, mma Tuzzio, Sophie Joseph, Amanda Radix, Mariana Weigel Munoz, Inez von Rege, Mary Dohrmann, Krish Surroy, Karen Bell, Gosia Charysz, Lucy Setters, Jenny Kovacs, Sandra Eriemo and Miche Tetley, who all contributed in some way to this book coming into existence. Thank you for being my amazing cheerleaders.

All the amazing people who have given me great feedback on the content, the cover and the title, who have waited in anticipation for this to be ready.

I am forever grateful lovelies x

Appendix 1 – The Mathematics of Music

Pythagoras found that it is possible to create a perfect harmony by adding an extra tone - a small half-step after the 4th tone in a 7 tone scale. Even though he was going against the accepted wisdom of the ancient Greeks – that the number 7 is sacred – he added this extra tone to make an 8 tone scale; in other words an *octave*. The perfect octave creates what Pythagoras defined as *harmonia*. It was a mark of how respected Pythagoras as a teacher was, that he was successfully able to introduce another number of significance (the 8 of an octave) that altered the cultural perceptions of his time.

The addition of this fifth tone, called the "fifth", "musical fifth" or "perfect fifth" is the tone that brings harmony. Pythagoras found the perfect fifth on his lyre when one string has a length that is two-thirds the length of the other. So playing this musical fifth brings with it a mathematical ratio of 3:2. When you divide 3 by 2 you get a value close to 1.618. 1.618 is the Golden Number or the Golden Mean, Phi.

He made three interesting observations:

1) when two strings of the same length are played, they have the same pitch (level of highness or lowness). The sound that they play (and the interval between the notes) is a called a **unison**. We hear unisons when a room of people or singers all sing the same note, that is a very powerful experience of *harmony* – this type of harmonious sound is called **consonant**. If you have ever been in a room when people are "Ohm-ing" (making an "Ohm" sound) together, you will have experienced a unison, consonant sounds; a *harmony*.

2) If two strings have different lengths, the sound is usually **dissonant** (disharmonious), except when:

   a) one string is exactly one-half of the length of the other string, its pitch (level of highness of lowness) is much higher, but they still sound **consonant** when played together. This interval is called an **octave.** So playing an octave is **harmonious.**

   b) one string has a length that is two-thirds the length of the other, the strings again sound **consonant** (harmonious) when played together and this interval is called a **Perfect Fifth**. We hear the Perfect Fifth, and its amazing harmony when we listen to Gregorian chants – religious chanting that goes back to the times of Byzantium.

   This **Perfect Fifth** contains the ratio 3:2 and gives us a number very very close to 1.618 (remember the further along the Fibonacci sequence we go, the closer to 1.618 we get, and we get to 1.618 from 89 onwards).

An octave is made of 13 notes. When you look at this on a piano keyboard, it looks like this:

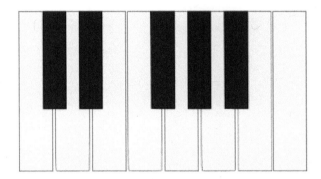

There are 8 white keys and 5 black keys (8 whole notes, and 5 half-step notes). Here we see again a ratio found in the Fibonacci sequence: 8 divided by 5 gives us a number very very close to 1.618 (remember the further along the Fibonacci sequence we go, the closer to 1.618 we get, and we get to 1.618 from 89 onwards).

Octaves can also be drawn into a circle – there is something called the Circle of Fifths. It shows the relationship with the notes in a chromatic scale. It looks like this:

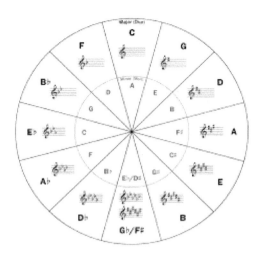

A famous saxophone player by the name of John Coltrane drew his own Circle of fifths, 5 octaves in a circle that generated a shape important in the mathematics and geometry we have been studying:

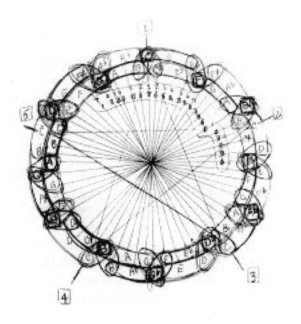

There is a remarkable connection between Phi in relation to the pentagram, as found in John Coltrane's Circle of Fifths.

A pentagram is a five sided shape. The angles of the 5 sides of the pentagram are in a ratio of 1.618. When we as humans stand with our legs apart, and our arms out from our bodies, and look at the position of our heads, hands and feet, we look like a star shape – and we fit perfectly into the dimensions of a pentagram. Quantum physicists have suggested that the Universe is in the shape of a dodecahedron – made of 12 pentagon faces. So basically, we are a smaller version of the exact same dimensions as the whole Universe! Like the Mandelbrot effect in action with the same shape being seen in our human bodies going all the way up to the Universe, making a beautiful harmonia as it does so.

187

Appendix 2 - The Love-Hate Rice Experiment

This is a great experiment to do with children, friends or loved ones.

1) Boil up some organic white rice.

2) Steam sterilize 3 glass jars that are the same size.

3) Put a couple of tablespoons of the boiled and cooled rice into each jar, and seal it.

4) Label one jar with the word LOVE, another with the word HATE and the third NEUTRAL. Keep them on a shelf at room temperature.

5) Every day for a week (or more), speak to the rice in the LOVE jar, saying lovely loving things like "you are so gorgeous, and healthy and pure, and I love how you help my body be healthy" etc. You will feel like an idiot btw, which is why having kids helps, as they love doing stuff like this, but it's worth pursuing. To the rice in the HATE jar, say awful thing like "I hate you, you disgust me, you are revolting, yuk" etc etc. Kids love this part the most. Ignore the NEUTRAL jar. That is your control jar.

6) After 5 days, you should notice a change in the rice – the LOVE rice usually stays pure white, the other two jars will be yellow, perhaps a little bit of mould on the rice in the NEUTRAL jar, more mould in the jar of HATE rice. The differences become more pronounced as the days go by.

This shows the power of thought – of intention – and also shows that if we send negative thoughts to ourselves, to the food we ingest, to others, we cause disease and disorder. If we do nothing, disease happens anyway. So this is an invitation to consciously send loving thoughts to ourselves, to others and to all that comes into contact with our bodies.

And to the world.

Appendix 3 - Glossary of Marketing Terms

Chemical free. Everything is made from chemicals. You and I, the food we eat, the plants we make our tea from, plant medicines are, as we have discussed, made of many naturally occurring plant chemicals working together. The question we face is whether they are *synthetic* including whether they are *petrochemicals.* Petrochemicals are synthetic chemicals made from petroleum, that known carcinogen.

Dermatologically tested. This simply means it has been tested for sensitivity on people, but does not mean that all its ingredients are 100% natural (and often aren't).

Enriched with Aloe Vera / Vitamin E / Coconut Oil / pure essential oils. This may be the case, but unless the product is 100% natural, the body will be receiving a mix of other chemical ingredients that will be considered "foreign objects" to the body, and trigger a disease response.

Environmentally (or eco) friendly. Products that are environmentally friendly aren't always 100% natural. These may be "plant-based", or "non-toxic" – have levels of toxicity that are said by the petrochemicals industry to be too low to have an environmental impact. This is a myth (see Non-Toxic below).

Natural. This is a word that is used a lot in misleading ways. A product might be "natural" in part, but actually, may also contain synthetic petrochemicals. Unless a product says it is 100% natural, it won't be.

Non-Toxic. There is a brand in the UK, Method, that prides itself on being non-toxic, but it is full of synthetic chemicals. Levels of toxicity are set by the petrochemicals industry, which suggests that even harmful toxic chemicals are "safe" in low doses, below a certain level. This is a myth. Homeopathy can use seemingly toxic substances safely, as it is working with the energy of those substances, not any physical substance. The low doses set by the petrochemicals industry involve low doses of physical substances, so these chemicals can build up in the body over time to toxic levels. One study found over 200 of these chemicals being passed from mothers to their unborn children via the umbilical cord. There are no true safe levels.

Parabens-free (or SLS free, or PEG free) Many companies will state that they are free of 3-4 core ingredients, but usually still contain *other* synthetic petrochemicals, but you are so delighted to see some of these ones aren't there, that you think your products are safe. No. Learn to read the ingredients list yourselves, and do a search on the ingredients for toxicity. Educating yourself in ways that help you make informed choices is the greatest gift you can give yourself.

Plant-based. The leading brand of such products in the UK, Ecover, that consumers think is natural, is actually "plant-based". That means whilst many of the ingredients are plant-based, it is not 100% natural, so there are *also* synthetic chemicals included in the ingredients. /

Pure this can mean *anything*. One company that has trademarked the word, uses Tetrasodium EDTA in their list of ingredients for sensitive cleansing wipes. Tetrasodium EDTA is made from formaldehyde, a known carcinogen. A range of baby wipes, sold as the "pure" version of that brand, and containing "99% water" also contains polysorbate-20. Polysorbate-20 is derived from sorbitol, a natural sugar alcohol, however it's not natural because it is treated with 20 parts of ethylene oxide, which can result in a by-product called 1,4-dioxane, a known carcinogen that is readily absorbed through the skin. High levels of this synthetic chemical were found to result in developmental and reproductive problems in animal studies, and at lower levels to skin allergies.

Sensitive. As with "dermatologically tested", this simply means it has been tested for sensitivity on people, but does not mean that all its ingredients are 100% natural (and often aren't).

"There is no evidence to suggest...." One of the most common phrases used by companies that often means "there might be evidence, but we are hiding it because we don't like it", or "no one has thoroughly researched the safety implications".

Resources

www.goldennumber.net provides great articles all about Phi in life, nature, mathematics, music, architecture and art.

www.toxipedia.org is a great website listing ingredients that can be toxic and why they can be toxic.

https://toxtown.nlm.nih.gov/index.php is a website supported by US National Library of Medicine that lists common toxic chemicals found in the workplace and in the home.

www.heartmath.org The HeartMath Institute in the US produces lots of research into the electromagnetic field, and coherence – a state of total and complete wellbeing physically, mentally, emotionally and spiritually. It has developed an app that enables individuals to monitor their levels of coherence and trains coaches in how to use the too.

www.projectcbd.org provides detailed information on the research into and use of CBD oil.

https://www.hri-research.org The Homeopathy Research Institute provides information on scientifically rigorous research proving that homeopathy works.

www.planetnatural.com shares organic gardening tips.

www.earthlinged.com Earthling Ed is a vegan activist and educator who provides tons of information on veganism, and the meat and dairy industries.

https://cleanwater.org/pfas-forever-chemicals provides information on PFAS: The Forever Chemicals

What The Health is an online film that can be viewed freely sharing some new knowledge about our diets.

www.thehappymovie.com Happy is a film that travels the world asking what makes us happy, drawing on research from positive psychology.

www.actionforhappiness.org is dedicated to helping us all live happier, healthier lives.

TED Talk: Sir Ken Robinson: Do Schools Kill Creativity?
https://www.ted.com/talks/
ken_robinson_says_schools_kill_creativity

www.strengthscope.com is a resource for this strengths based assessment tool.

www.viacharacter.org is a free resource for identifying your strengths.

References

David Hamilton (2008) *How Your Mind Can Heal Your Body* Hay House

Gregg Braden talking about the Mandelbrot Set
https://www.youtube.com/watch?v=W4N08QMwylE

Music & Mathematics
http://www.phys.uconn.edu/~gibson/Notes/Section3_2/Sec3_2.htm

Cymascope research into musical sounds
http://www.cymascope.com/cyma_research/musicology.html

Lynne McTaggart (2001) *The Field* Thorsons Element

Marcus Chown (2008) in his book *Quantum Theory Cannot Hurt You*
Faber and Faber

Jan Wicherink (2004) *Souls of Distortion Awakening* Published Online
https://www.goodreads.com/book/show/
1935772.Souls_of_Distortion_Awakening

Winter,D, Donavan, B., and Jones, M. (2012) *Compressions, The Hydrogen Atom and Phase Conjugation* The General Science Journal
http://www.fractalfield.com/mathematicsoffusion/

Xiang, J. et al (2014) *Effect of ultrasound sonication on clonogenic survival and mitochondria of ovarian cancer cells in the presence of methylene blue* Journal of Ultrasound Medicine 33 (10) 1755

Chevalier, G. et al (2012) *Earthing: Health Implications of Reconnecting the Human Body to the Earth's Surface Electrons* Journal of Environmental and Public Health

https://www.ncbi.nlm.nih.gov/pmc/articles/PMC3265077/

Oschman, J.L et al (2015) *The effects of grounding (earthing) on inflammation, the immune response, wound healing, and prevention and treatment of chronic inflammatory and autoimmune diseases* Journal of Inflammation Research

https://www.ncbi.nlm.nih.gov/pmc/articles/PMC4378297/

Kate Birch (2019) *Glyphosate Free* Kate Birch

Kogevinas M. Probable carcinogenicity of glyphosate *BMJ* 2019; 365 :l1613 doi:10.1136/bmj.l1613

https://www.bmj.com/content/365/bmj.l1613

Biwal, S. & Harvey, C. (2011) *Broccoli's effect on damaged lungs* Journal of Science Translational Medicine DOI: 10.1126/scitranslmed.3002042

Frazzetto, G. (2008) *The drugs don't work for everyone. Doubts about the efficacy of antidepressants renews debates over the medicalization of common distress.* EMBO Reports: Science and Society 9 (7)

Cannell, J.J. et al., (2006) *Epidemic influenza and vitamin D* Journal of Epidemiology and Infection (134) 6

Dr Mercola: article summarising research into vitamin D and the immune system

https://articles.mercola.com/sites/articles/archive/2017/02/27/vitamin-d-better-than-flu-vaccine.aspx

Dr David Jockers The Truth About Cancer: *Vanilla is a potent anti-mutagenic agent*

https://thetruthaboutcancer.com/vanilla-is-a-potent-anti-mutagenic-agent/

Hyun-Joo Jung et al. (2010) *Assessment of the anti-angiogenic, anti-inflammatory and antinociceptive properties of ethyl vanillin* Archives of Pharmacal Research, 33 (2)

https://link.springer.com/article/10.1007%2Fs12272-010-0217-2

King, A.A. et al., (2007) *Antimutagenicity of cinnamaldehyde and vanillin in human cells: Global gene expression and possible role of DNA damage and repair* Mutation Research, 616 (1-2)

https://www.sciencedirect.com/science/article/pii/S0027510706003344

Soulaidopoulos S, Tsiogka A, Chrysohoou C, Lazarou E, Aznaouridis K, Doundoulakis I, Tyrovola D, Tousoulis D, Tsioufis K, Vlachopoulos C, Lazaros G. *Overview of Chios Mastic Gum (Pistacia lentiscus) Effects on Human Health.* Nutrients. 2022 Jan 28;14(3):590. doi: 10.3390/nu14030590. PMID: 35276949; PMCID: PMC8838553.
https://www.ncbi.nlm.nih.gov/pmc/articles/PMC8838553/

Anthony William (2015) *Medical Medium: Secrets Behind Chronic and Mystery Illness and How to Finally Heal* Hay House

Anthony William (2016) *Life Changing Foods: Save Yourself and the Ones You Love with the Hidden Healing power of Fruits and Vegetables* Hay House

David Hoffman (1983) *Holistic Herbal: A Safe and Practical Guide to Making and Using Herbal Remedies* Thorsons

Dr Ganmaa Davassambuu's research into modern milk and estrogenic cancers: https://harvardmagazine.com/2007/05/modern-milk.html

Zeng, F. et al (2017) *Occupational exposure to pesticides and other biocides and risk of thyroid cancer* Journal of Occupational and Environmental Medicine 74 (7)

Wright, Carolanne (2017) *New Research Links Hand Sanitizer Use with Thyroid Cancer* Wake Up World https://wakeup-world.com/2017/04/28/new-research-links-hand-sanitizer-use-with-thyroid-cancer/

Schulte, E.M., et al (2015) *Which foods may be addictive? The roles of processing, fat content and glycemic load* PLOS Journal http://journals.plos.org/plosone/article?id=10.1371/journal.pone.0117959

Furlong. E.T., et al *Nationwide reconnaissance of contaminants of emerging concern in source and treated drinking waters of the United States: Pharmaceuticals* Science of The Total Environment, Vol 579, 1 Feb 2017, pages 1629-1642

Boxall, A., *et al*. 2011. *Targeted Monitoring For Human Pharmaceuticals In Vulnerable Source And Final Waters*. Drinking Water Inspectorate Project No. WD0805 (Ref DWI 70/2/231). http://dwi.defra.gov.uk/research/completed-research/reports/DWI70_2_231.pdf

Organic Consumers Factsheet on 1,4-Dioxane: https://www.organicconsumers.org/sites/default/files/downloads/

DioxaneFacts080314.pdf

Sam Roe & Patricia Callahan, *Distorting Science* 9 May 2012, Chicago Tribune
http://www.chicagotribune.com/news/watchdog/ct-met-flames-science-20120509-story.html#page=1

Patricia Callahn & Michael Hawthorne, *Chemicals in the crib,* 28 December 2012, Chicago Tribune

Activism regarding scented products: http://www.nbcnews.com/id/23836093/ns/health-behavior/t/odor-tyrants-those-sensitive-scent-fight-back/#.WrpR462ZO8U

Fragrance is the new second hand smoke:
https://www.huffingtonpost.ca/lisa-borden/natural-fragrances_b_14086978.html

Sarantis. H., et al., (2010): *Not So Sexy: The Health Risks of Secret Chemicals in Fragrance* Campaign for Safe Cosmetics

https://www.ewg.org/research/body-burden-pollution-newborns#.WrpMXa2ZO8U Environmental Working Group, July 12, 2005 Body Burden: The Pollution in Newborns

Mogensen, S.W. et al (2017) *The Introduction of Diptheria-Tetanus-Pertussis and Oral Polio Vaccine Among Young Infants in an Urban African Community: A Natural Experment* EBioMedicine 2017

Dr Tetyana Obukhanych, 2012. *Illusion: How Vaccination Compromises our Natural Immunity and What We Can Do To Regain Our Health*

Trevor Gunn, 2014 *A Mother's Vaccine Dilemma – How to Make Your Choice With Confidence* Holistic Promotions

Mumps Outbreak at Harvard https://www.huffingtonpost.com/entry/mumps-outbreak-at-harvard-why-do-vaccinated-people-get-sick_us_57276bc7e4b0b49df6abc402

Leaving Traces: The hidden hazardous chemicals in outdoor gear Greenpeace Product Test 2016 http://detox-outdoor.org/assets/uploads/Report_Product_Testing.pdf

NASA: Hacking the planet https://climate.nasa.gov/news/1066/just-5-questions-hacking-the-planet/#:~:text="Solar

Cloud seeding https://en.wikipedia.org/wiki/Cloud_seeding#:~:text=Cloud seeding is undertaken by,their ability to attract moisture.

Laura Kuhl, 2022 *Dodging silver bullets: how cloud seeding could go wrong* Bulletin of the Atomic Scientists https://thebulletin.org/2022/08/dodging-silver-bullets-how-cloud-seeding-could-go-wrong/

Luminet et al., (2003) *Is the Universe a dodecahedron?* Nature 425 593.

Teens + Social Media = Depression? Is Social Media Affecting Mental Health? (2018)

https://www.psycom.net/depression-teens-social-media

Morris, D. (2017) *Facebook Admits Social Media Can Harm Your Mental Health* Fortune Magazine

http://fortune.com/2017/12/16/facebook-admits-social-media-can-harm-your-mental-health/

Schrobsdorff, S. (2016) *Teen Depression and Anxiety: the Kids Are Not Alright* Time Magazine

http://time.com/4547322/american-teens-anxious-depressed-overwhelmed/

Weller, C. (2018) *Silicon Valley parents are raising their kids tech-free – and it should be a red flag* Business Insider UK

http://uk.businessinsider.com/silicon-valley-parents-raising-their-kids-tech-free-red-flag-2018-2

Kahneman, D. & Deaton, A. (2010) *High income improves evaluation of life but not emotional well-being.* Proceedings of the National Academy of Sciences of the United States of America 107 (38)

The Alternative Daily (2016) *Study: $75,000 Actually Buys Happiness (but what about more?)*

https://www.thealternativedaily.com/does-income-matter-to-happiness/

About Danica

Danica (pronounced De-nit-sa) spent years working in pharmacies and started her training to become a Pharmacist. Her life took an unexpected turn, and she studied psychology before becoming a training specialist, strengths coach and energy healer along the way.

Her love of medicine remained, and she came to study natural approaches to medicine and health. She is now a homeopath, Founder of Blueprint Essences, and also the Golden Spiral International School of Homeopathy, and author of several other books.

A thought leader & health visionary, she draws upon all of her learning & experience to share new ways of thinking about health and medicine. She lives in Lewes, England with her son.